Copyright © 2018 by ECO Publishing

Publisher

ECO Publishing

4 Rattlesnake Canyon Road

Rodeo, New Mexico 88056

Tel. (575) 557-5757

(575) 545-5307

Fax (575) 557-7575

E-mail: desertmuseum@gmail.com

Layout and Design

Charles F. Smith

www.copperheadinstitute.org

charlessmith35@gmail.com

Artwork and Distribution Maps

(artwork pages 14, 19, 20, 21, blank page digital art)

Charles F. Smith

ISBN 978-1-1938850-58-5

Printed in Korea

Rattlesnakes *of the* Grand Canyon

Gordon W. Schuett

Charles F. Smith

Bob Ashley

The Grand Canyon fills me with awe. It is beyond comparison— beyond description; absolutely unparalleled throughout the wide world ... Let this great wonder of nature remain as it now is. Do nothing to mar its grandeur, sublimity and loveliness. You cannot improve on it. But what you can do is to keep it for your children, your children's children, and all who come after you, as the one great sight which every American should see.

- President Theodore Roosevelt (1903)

Contents

Foreword

Geoffrey C. Carpenter and Andrew T. Holycross

Legendary creatures of the American West, rattlesnakes are feared by many, but loved and appreciated by others. Whether through fear or excitement, an encounter with a rattlesnake will usually get the old heart pumping. A visit to the Grand Canyon may involve a brief stop at rim overviews, short hikes lasting a few hours, multi-day backpacking treks, or a whitewater rafting and camping adventure along the Colorado River in the bottom of the canyon lasting weeks. During any of these activities, visitors may encounter one of several species of rattlesnakes found in this region.

Having spent considerable time backpacking and rafting in the Grand Canyon, we have encountered many rattlesnakes in various settings of the canyon. As professional herpetologists, one source of our frustration has been seeing these beautiful creatures misidentified in communications, publications, and other sources, even by those with extensive outdoor experience or professional training in biology. Arizona is home to nineteen kinds of rattlesnakes, yet a visitor to the Grand Canyon will be fortunate if they see only one or two of the eight covered in this book. The vast majority of visitors will see none at all, as these snakes spend much of their lives under cover — their safety and long-term survival depends on remaining undetected by enemies and possible predators.

The distribution of rattlesnakes in the Grand Canyon and surrounding region is limited to particular areas. Some are found primarily within the canyon and along the river corridor, while others are confined to the plateaus above the canyon's north and south rims. In most cases, however, their distributions do not overlap. Thus, by considering geographic distribution in concert with the various identifying characteristics provided in this book, visitors should be able to determine the type of rattlesnake they have encountered.

Schuett, Smith, and Ashley have compiled an important reference to the rattlesnakes that occur in and nearby the Grand Canyon. Their book serves as a valuable resource to visitors who wish to enhance their appreciation of the canyon's natural history. With the aid of this guide, visitors that have the good fortune to observe a rattlesnake will not only be able to correctly identify it, but also learn about many aspects of its fascinating biology from these rattlesnake experts. It is an excellent and lightweight addition to a backpack or dry bag!

Grand Canyon Rattlesnake. Artwork by Tell Hicks.

Acknowledgments

We thank the many individuals who have assisted us with this book project. In particular, Geoffrey Carpenter, Martin Feldner, and Andrew Holycross gave us their advice, information on the Grand Canyon National Park (GRCA), and critically reviewed the entire manuscript. We are grateful to Geoffrey and Andrew for their foreword.

The rattlesnake paintings by Tell Hicks grace each of the eight species accounts. He has beautifully captured the essence of these animals; we are in awe of his artistic gifts. The book cover is Tell's painting of the iconic Grand Canyon Rattlesnake, *Crotalus abyssus*.

This book has many wonderful images and photographs owing to the generosity of many talented individuals. We greatly appreciate their contributions, especially Martin J. Feldner, Brendan O'Connor, and William Wells.

Photographic Credits
Timothy Allen (page 84)
Bob Ashley (book cover background photo of Grand Canyon; 27; 31; 41)
Randall Babb (pages 67; 69)
Alex Bentley (page 91)
Patrik Blomsten (page 24 middle)
Michael Cardwell (pages 22; 24 top; 113)
Ed Cassano (pages 54; 62; 96)
Dale DeNardo (page 57)
Martin Feldner (pages 29; 30; 33-35; 43 top; 44 bottom; 45-46; 48; 55-56; 61; 95; 102)
Noah Fields (page 92)
Kris Haas (page 37)
Bryan Hughes (page 53)
Nicholas Lehnberg (page 38)
Jesse Meik (page 23)
Jeff Miller (page 116)
Sam Murray (page 89)
Brendan O'Connor (pages 34; 69; 101; 104-105; 107-108)
Louis Porras (pages 34; 43 bottom; 44)
John Slone (page 24 bottom)
Charles Smith (pages 71; 90)
Matthew Smith (page 76)
Will Wells (pages 30; 57; 60; 68; 70; 81-82; 90; 103; 114-115)
Wolfgang Wüster (page 71)

Introduction

Rattlesnakes are an indisputable American icon and among the best recognized group of reptiles in the United States and throughout the world. The cultural importance of these reptiles dates back to our earliest ancestors who depicted them in their petroglyphs, cave drawings (pictographs), baskets, and other art forms, including ritual dances and religious ceremonies (Klauber, 1932; Reiserer, 2016). No doubt, rattlesnakes have played a significant role in the spiritual lives and social fabric of the ancient

Native Americans inhabiting the Grand Canyon and nearby regions. In modern times, rattlesnakes have a pivotal role in providing insights to the study

Granaries made by ancient Native Americans at Nankoweap above the Colorado River, Grand Canyon National Park. Photo by Mark Lellouch (NPS).

of medicine and evolution (Mackessy & Castoe, 2016). They also are important to our understanding of the complex ecology of the Grand Canyon and Colorado Plateau; their protection and conservation are key topics of current research (Davis et al., 2016a; Douglas et al., 2016; Nowak & Greene, 2016).

COLORADO RIVER BASIN, COLORADO PLATEAU, ORIGIN OF THE GRAND CANYON & GEOLOGY

The Grand Canyon is situated in northwestern Arizona and spans two counties. It is part of the extensive Colorado River Basin (see image below) and Colorado Plateau (image on page 14), which have been forming over the past 40 million years. It is a steep-sided canyon (river valley), in part, carved and eroded by the Colorado River and its tributaries of the Colorado Plateau. The Grand Canyon is roughly 277 miles (446 km) long, up to 18 miles (29 km) wide, and attains depths of 1 mile (1.6 km) or greater.

The Colorado Plateau is a large area that is approximately centered on the Four Corners region comprised of portions of Arizona, Utah, Colorado, and New Mexico. The Colorado Plateau spans an area of 130,000 square miles (337,000 km²) and about 90% of this area is drained by the Colorado River and its main tributaries, namely the Green River, San Juan River, and Little Colorado River.

The Grand Canyon had its origin ~17 million years ago (mya). During the development of the Grand Canyon, there were many episodes of uplifts and periods of erosion, which exposed strata of the Proterozoic Eon (250 to 541 mya) and Paleozoic Era (540 to 252 mya). Roughly, the rock exposures of the Grand Canyon can be partitioned into three major categories (oldest to youngest: Vishnu Basement Rocks, Grand Canyon Supergroup Rocks, and Layered Paleozoic Rocks, respectively), which range in age from 2 billion years at the bottom of the Inner Gorge (Vishnu Schist) to 230 million years on the top or Rim (Kaibab Limestone). Also, there are gaps (unconformities) in the geologic record which indicate periods in which deposits were not occurring; some are substantial periods of time (e.g., hundreds of millions of years and greater). The Great Unconformity represents a period of 1.2 to 1.6 billion years.

For more details of the origin and geology of the Grand Canyon, see Karlstrom et al. (2014). Formation of the Grand Canyon 5 to 6 million years ago through integration of older palaeocanyons. Nature Geoscience 7: 239–244.

For books and DVDs on the history and geology of the Grand Canyon and Grand Canyon National Park (GRCA), visit this website: https://shop.grandcanyon.org/collections/gifts-collectables-collectables/.

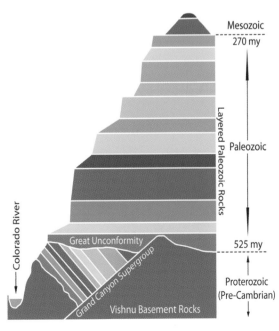

HUMAN INFLUENCE & CULTURE

The Grand Canyon is contained within and managed by Grand Canyon National Park, the Kaibab National Forest, Grand Canyon-Parashant National Monument, the Hualapai Tribal Nation, the Havasupai People, and the Navajo Nation. This area has been continuously inhabited by endemic peoples for thousands of years. Its inhabitants built settlements within the canyon and its many caves. The Ancestral Puebloans considered the Grand Canyon a holy site and made pilgrimages to the area. It appears that the first Europeans to visit and explore the Grand Canyon occurred in the mid-16th century (circa 1540).

Archaeological remains of ancient indigenous Indians and other ethnic groups found in the Grand Canyon National Park include: Paleo-Indian, Archaic, Basketmaker, Ancestral Puebloan (Kayenta and Virgin Branches), Cohonina, Cerbat, Pai, Southern Paiute, Zuni, Hopi, Navajo, and Euro-American.

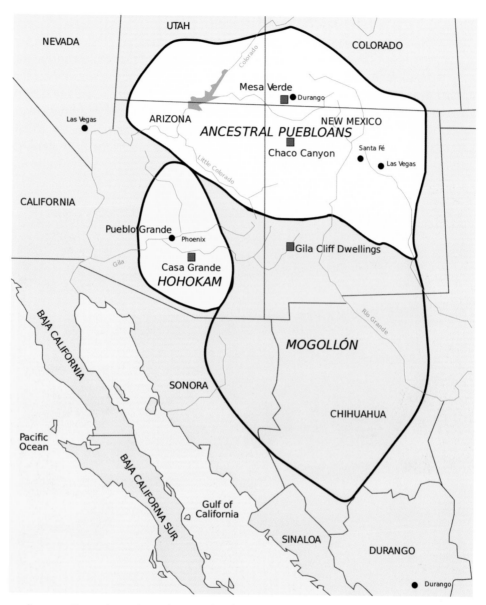

As mentioned, rattlesnakes and other reptiles undoubtedly had an important role in the culture of early indigenous Americans, which can be seen today in the remnants of their art, including ancient pots, baskets, weavings, and petroglyphs.

You can learn more about the ancient peoples of the Grand Canyon and nearby areas at these websites:

www.grandcanyon.org/shop/online-store/ancient-landscapes-colorado-plateau
www.nps.gov/subjects/swscience/ancestral-puebloan.htm

GRAND CANYON NATIONAL PARK

Grand Canyon National Park (GRCA), officially designated in 1919, is located in the northwestern region of the state of Arizona, United States. The central and most famous feature of the park is the Grand Canyon, one of the wonders of the world. The park itself is impressively large, spanning 1,217,262 acres (4,926.08 km²) of unincorporated area in two large counties (Coconino County and Mohave County). The general public typically gains access to the park at the North and South Rims, (the remainder of the park is remote and difficult to access), and most who visit GRCA enter via the South Rim using Arizona State Route 64. Remarkably, GRCA hosted about six million visitors in 2016.

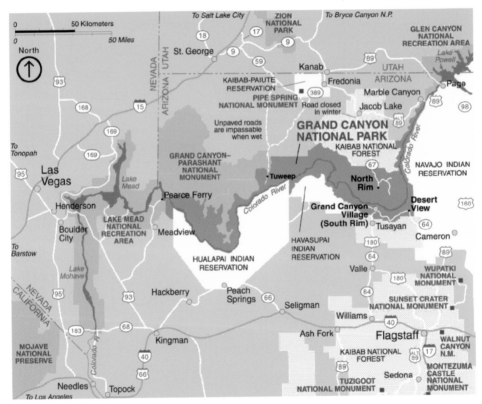

GRCA map is derived from nps.gov.

For more details on the GRCA, visit these websites:

www.grandcanyon.org
www.nps.gov/grca/index.htm

A PRIMER ON RATTLESNAKES & THEIR RELATIVES

With only a few exceptions, researchers know little about the day-to-day lives of rattlesnakes, especially regarding individuals, owing to the challenge that they are mostly secretive and unassuming. Contrary to popular views, most species of rattlesnakes do not sound with their famous rattling display unless provoked. They primarily rely on camouflage, a subterranean lifestyle, and nocturnality. In their habitats, including the GRCA, many people have walked right past rattlesnakes without their detection or nary a conflict.

Most people have never had the experience of seeing one of these majestic animals undisturbed in nature. During your visit to the GRCA you might have the privilege of seeing a rattlesnake, perhaps even one of its true icons, the Grand Canyon Rattlesnake (*Crotalus abyssus*).

In this book, we will provide you with background information and intriguing facts about rattlesnakes and their close relatives. We will highlight the species that live in or nearby the Grand Canyon, including the beautiful Grand Canyon Rattlesnake.

Rattlesnake Diagnosis: What is a Rattlesnake?

Rattlesnakes are members of a larger group of venomous snakes called vipers (lineage Viperidae), and within that group, more specifically, biologists recognize a more exclusive lineage (group) identified as pitvipers (Crotalinae). So-called true vipers (Viperinae) are a widely distributed group from Africa, Europe and throughout Asia. True vipers are entirely absent from the New World, which includes the United States. Species of true vipers that are well known to the public include the Common Adder (*Vipera berus*) from Europe, the Puff Adder (*Bitis arietans*) and Gaboon Viper (*B. gabonica*) from Africa, and Russell's Viper (*Daboia russelii*) from throughout Asia.

Unlike the true vipers, pitvipers are found in both the Old and New Worlds. This group is identified by a suite of unique characters, but the most notable (and the one which bears their namesake) is a small opening or depression (pit) located on the loreal scale on each side of the head between the eyes and nostrils. These pits are part of a heat-sensing organ complex, and they likely aid the snake in locating and subjugating prey, particularly warm-blooded (endothermic) vertebrates such as mammals and birds.

Thermal-Sensitive Facial Pits

The group or clade we call pitvipers gained their namesake by the facial pits located near their nostrils. Experts agree that these pits are part of a larger complex internal organ system which is involved in thermal reception (sensing infra-red thermal radiation). Location, size, and shape of the loreal scale and external pit

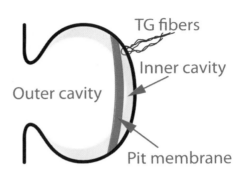

The yellow arrow denotes the location of one (left side) of the two "pits" of the heat-sensing organs of this rattlesnake.

vary among species. It is widely believed that this thermal sensing organ system evolved to detect warm-blooded prey; however, other functions include thermoregulation and short- and long-distance navigation. Other snakes, such as boas and pythons, have independently evolved similar thermal pit structures. This is termed convergent evolution.

For more information on the topic of thermal reception in pitvipers and other snakes, see references below:

Harvey B. Lillywhite's fascinating book, *How Snakes Work: Structure, Function and Behavior of the World's Snakes*. Oxford University Press (2014).

Richard C. Goris (2011). Infrared organs of snakes: an integral part of vision. Journal of Herpetology 45: 2-14.

Venomous versus Poisonous?

Rattlesnakes and all other pitvipers are venomous. It is incorrect to refer to them as poisonous snakes. The difference between poison and venom is more than mere semantics. The primary difference is the manner in which a species uses its chemical defense. Venom is injected, such as through a rattlesnake's fangs. But it also can be delivered by a sting from a bee or jellyfish, or a jab from a lionfish's spine. These and most other venoms are delivered in a liquid state. On the other hand, because it is not injected, a poison is either ingested or inhaled; also, poisons can be in a liquid, solid or gas state. Many kinds of plants have poisonous fruits or seeds, and eating (ingesting) them can be dangerous, potentially causing severe illness or even death.

Venom in rattlesnakes and other pitvipers travels through a specific set of highly modified teeth termed fangs. Fangs are linked to the venom glands located behind the head. In both true vipers and pitvipers, these can be large and

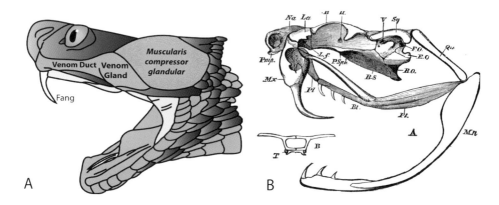

A

B

(a) The venom gland in relation to the fang. (b) A delineation of a rattlesnake head skeleton with an intact fang.

moveable (hinged), whereas in other venomous snakes, such as cobras and sea snakes, the fangs are relatively fixed. Fangs of rattlesnakes are replaced regularly.

For more details on pitvipers, rattlesnakes, and venom, see these references: Greene (1997), Lillywhite (2014), and Mackessy & Castoe (2016).

Deep History of Rattlesnakes & other Pitvipers
All evidence to date indicates that pitvipers had their origin and evolved in Asia. Over millions of years, these early ancestors of rattlesnakes presumably migrated to the New World by way of the famous land connection called the Bering Land Bridge (Malhotra et al., 2010). Pitvipers diversified greatly in the New World in both temperate and tropical environments. The closest living relatives to rattlesnakes are members of the genus *Agkistrodon*, such as Copperheads, Cottonmouths, and Cantils (Malhotra et al., 2010; Wüster, 2016). Cantils are restricted to the western coastal regions of Mesoamerica, from southern Sonora (Mexico) to western Costa Rica (Porras et al., 2014).

Fossils of snakes, including pitvipers, in North America are rare, but examples of their vertebrae indicate that rattlesnakes and their pitviper ancestors were present in North America during the Pliocene Epoch (~5 million years ago) and quite likely much earlier (Brattstrom, 1954, 1964; Holman, 2000).

Rattlesnake Evolution & Relationships
Current research indicates that rattlesnakes evolved in the New World. Though authorities are not in full agreement, it appears that there are about forty-eight extant species of rattlesnakes (Reptile Database, 2017, www.reptile-database.org/; see Dreslik et al., 2017). Two genera of rattlesnakes are accepted, *Crotalus* and *Sistrurus*, though only members of *Crotalus* are found in the Grand Canyon and nearby areas.

The tree below is an example of rattlesnake relationships. This tree represents species of the western group (clade), which includes the Grand Canyon Rattlesnake (*Crotalus abyssus*) and its closest living (extant) relatives. There are six species in this group, of which four are found in Arizona (Schuett et al., 2016).

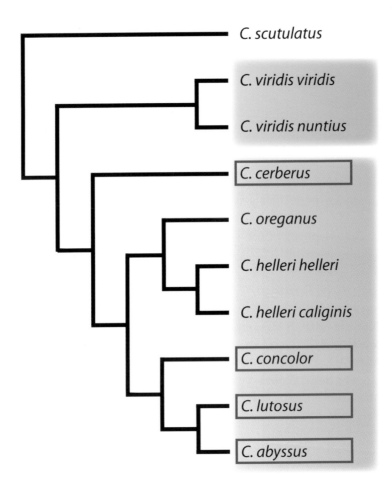

A phylogenetic tree of the western rattlesnake group. Red rectangles denote the 4 species that occur in Arizona; 3 occur in the Grand Canyon and nearby areas. The Prairie Rattlesnake (*C. viridis*) is sister to the western group. Modified from Davis (2016).

THE RATTLE

The genus name for the vast majority of rattlesnakes is *Crotalus* (Greek, krotalon), which refers to the rattle. All rattlesnakes have a rattle, though there is enormous variation in size and appearance. The visible rattle itself is a multi-segmented set of interlocking resonators that has no parallel among bioacoustic organs in the animal kingdom.

What Is It Made Of? How Does It Form?

The rattle itself is largely composed of the protein keratin. Keratin is found in fingernails and toenails, hair, and other body parts. In other examples, keratin is a major part of hooves, horns, antlers, and scales.

Below we quote Meik & Schuett (2016, p. 282) on the development of the rattle:

> The rattle consists of multiple interlocking segments of exuviated stratum corneum [skin] that have been molded from the living epithelial tissues of the matrix, specifically the stratum granulosum. Thus, a new segment is added each time the snake sheds its skin. Each new rattle segment nests inside the previously shed segment, to which it grips loosely with the fluted or corrugated "claws" that constitute the proximal constriction of each rattle segment. In addition to the gripping claw, each segment has expanded lobes nesting slightly offset anteriorly within previously shed segments; collectively these components make a distinctive buzzing sound when vibrated rapidly. Rattlesnakes are born with a lobe-less segment, the pre-button, which is not retained with the first shed, or ecdysis. Through ontogeny [age], two additional lobes are added to the matrix, creating the molds for each shed that allow successive rattle segments to interlock with each other.

How Did The Rattle Evolve?

The rattlesnake rattle is arguably one of the most complex and unique natural sound-producing structures known to science. As an integrative organ system (which includes the internal style, matrix, and rattle muscles), like eyes, ears, and other examples, the rattle appears highly unlikely to have evolved in a single evolutionary step for sound production only ("warning device"). Recent analyses have promoted the view that the early (incipient) rattle was small, not segmented, and was probably used for functions other than sound making in defensive acts (i.e., caudal luring, a type of mimicry or mimetic resemblance used by primitive rattlesnakes). Today, especially in large-bodied species, the rattle is irrefutably used as a defensive ("warning") device. However, few studies have rigorously investigated that function which seems so obvious to us.

A newborn rattlesnake within the amniotic membrane; note the tail tip and rattle. Photo by M. Cardwell.

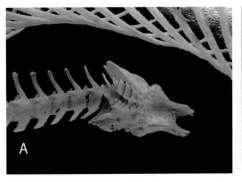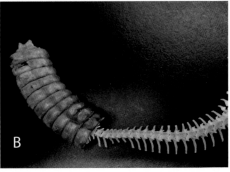

Rattlesnake skeletons. (a) Caudal vertebrae with style and matrix intact (no rattle attached). (b) Caudal vertebrae with rattle attached (style and matrix not visible). Photo from Meik & Schuett (2016).

Given that the rattle has probably had a long evolutionary history, the most robust hypothesis is an integrative one that embraces both mimetic and defensive influences on its development. In this view, the early proto-rattle was a modestly enlarged, conical terminal scale that was sloughed during molts. Under selection, this structure initially evolved in the context of both defensive tail vibrations and caudal luring. Ultimately, there was selection on segments not to slough off but to interlock and form a string with each shed. This scenario likely occurred in a series of stages; however, it cannot be directly tested owing to the fact that, among other things, fossil impressions of rattles have never been found, nor can we reconstruct evolution histories. Rather, as in other areas of science that involve deep time, we must rely on inference and comparative methods as tools to address such evolutionary puzzles.

Details of the rattle origin and its evolutionary development will likely contribute to our general understanding of and appreciation for evolutionary novelties (Wagner, 2015). For recent information on rattle development and evolution see Reiserer & Schuett (2016) and Meik & Schuett (2016).

REPRODUCTION

Rattlesnakes reproduce in similar ways to ordinary animals; that is, by way of viviparity, which translates to having live-birth. Though there are a few exceptions, most viperid snakes, including rattlesnakes, do not lay eggs. Litter size and size of the progeny in rattlesnakes is largely dependent on the size of the mother and the species. Litter size is highly variable, but 5-15 is an average range for rattlesnakes. Interestingly, rattlesnakes are good mothers; they remain with and defend their offspring after birth and until they have their first shed or molt (see Greene et al., 2002). Post-birth parental behavior is rare in other groups of snakes. Reproduction in rattlesnakes has recently been reviewed by Taylor & Booth (2016).

Facing page artwork by Tell Hicks

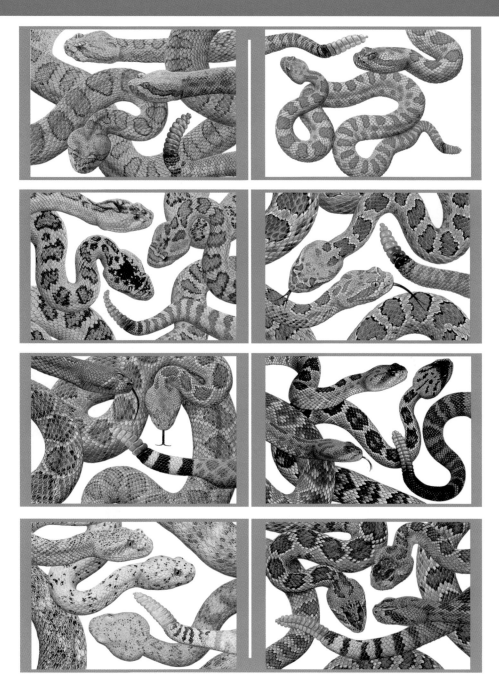

Grand Canyon Rattlesnake

Crotalus abyssus

COMMON NAMES

With no uncertainty, the Grand Canyon Rattlesnake and other species of rattlesnakes were revered and understood by the various ancestral peoples who have occupied the Grand Canyon and its surrounding environs. However, to modern science, the Grand Canyon Rattlesnake is a newcomer and was not formally described until 1930, by the self-taught snake expert Laurence M. Klauber (Klauber, 1930, 1972). Owing to the fact that most of the specimens examined by Laurence Klauber originated from the Grand Canyon, he designated the vernacular or common name for this undescribed rattlesnake as Grand Canyon Rattlesnake. That name remains the accepted common name today. However, because some adult individuals of this species are pink, salmon, or vermilion in coloration, it is sometimes referred to as the Grand Canyon Pink Rattlesnake or just Pink Rattlesnake. Nonetheless, most individuals are not this coloration and instead are shades of yellow and brown (see below, *Pattern & coloration*); thus, as a diagnostic tool, strict reliance on color, especially salmon, vermilion, or pink, is fraught with problems and will most likely lead to misidentification (see below, *Similar looking species*).

SCIENTIFIC NAMES

The scientific name of the Grand Canyon Rattlesnake has undergone change with increasing study and analysis. The original binomial name designated by Klauber (1930) was *Crotalus confluentus abyssus*, and several years later Klauber himself reassigned the name of this rattlesnake as a subspecies of the Prairie Rattlesnake, *Crotalus viridis abyssus*.

Decades later, researchers using mitochondrial DNA sequence evidence designated the Grand Canyon Rattlesnake (*Crotalus viridis abyssus*) as a subspecies of the Western Rattlesnake, *Crotalus oreganus abyssus* (see Pook et al., 2000; Ashton & de Queiroz, 2001). Currently, owing to additional evidence from DNA sequence data and modern morphological analyses, the Grand Canyon Rattlesnake is recognized as a full species, and its binomial name has been adjusted to *Crotalus abyssus* (see Douglas et al., 2002; Davis, 2012).

Although frustrating to some people, these types of name or taxonomic changes are not unusual and have occurred in many other groups of animals (and plants); rather than a nuisance, these changes indicate healthy progress in our scientific understanding and knowledge. Scientific names of all organisms are best viewed as hypotheses that are (and should be) constantly challenged and tested by biologists.

DESCRIPTION

Body size

Older adults of the Grand Canyon Rattlesnakes can be medium- to large-sized snakes, sometimes attaining a maximum total length of nearly 1000 mm, or about 3 feet (Feldner et al., 2016a).

Sexual size dimorphism (SSD) is a common phenomenon in rattlesnakes, typically with males attaining greater sizes than females, which is the situation in the Grand Canyon Rattlesnake. It also appears that there is local variability in size. Individuals that occur along the Colorado River tend to be robust and achieve relatively large sizes, but those that occupy the re-

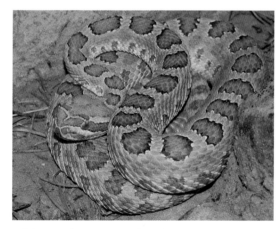

Adult Grand Canyon Rattlesnake. Note that its color pattern remains vivid. Not all individuals are pink and faded. Photo by M. Feldner.

gion between Lee's Ferry and the confluence of the Little Colorado River are variable in size and sexual maturity is achieved at a smaller total length (B. Starrett, personal communication). Outside of the Grand Canyon NP, populations that occur below the Vermilion Cliffs and from the vicinity of the Paria River and south to the Kaiparowits Plateau in Utah do not appear to attain the larger sizes of snakes from within the canyon at river level and higher elevations of both the North and South Rims. Size differences may be due to habitat quality, differing prey densities or prey base, temperatures and conditions limiting activity and effectively shortening season length, local adaptation, and possibly competition with other snake species (Feldner et al., 2016a).

The mean (average) total length of newborns is 250 mm, which is similar to other members of the Western Rattlesnake complex (see accounts in Schuett et al., 2016). The smallest pregnant female measured 684 mm in total length, and sexual maturity in males is likely at a similar size.

Pattern & coloration
Typical of all members of the Western Rattlesnake group, newborn and juvenile Grand Canyon Rattlesnakes display dark blotches on a light silver-gray background.

Grand Canyon Rattlesnakes. (a) Neonate. Photo by W. Wells. (b) Juvenile. Photo by M. Feldner.

With sexual maturity, which is reached within about 4 years, the ground color of some individuals undergoes a dramatic change to salmon, vermilion, or pink, with coloration of the pink hues as diagnostic for the species, earning it the name Grand Canyon Pink as often introduced to visitors of the GRCA. However, extensive observations (>105 individuals) of this species in the Grand Canyon and in other parts of its range (including Utah) have shown that the most common ground color for adults is yellowish-tan, pale gray, pale brown, or buff (see Feldner et al., 2016a).

An extraordinarily beautiful example of an adult Grand Canyon Rattlesnake. Photo by B. Ashley.

Venom

Since its description in 1930, various studies have been conducted on the venom of the Grand Canyon Rattlesnake and its close relatives. Some of this work was aimed to better understand its relations to other members of the Western Rattlesnake group.

The venom of the Grand Canyon Rattlesnake has been shown to be similar to venom of the Great Basin Rattlesnake (*Crotalus lutosus*). Both species show high metalloproteinase activity (a protease enzyme) and are considerably lower in toxicity (LD_{50}) than another close relative, the Midget Faded Rattlesnake (*Crotalus concolor*), which has potent neurotoxins (concolor toxin) and myotoxins (Mackessy & Castoe, 2016). Recent work in Stephen Mackessy's lab shows that high metalloproteinase activity is incompatible with high toxicity neurotoxins, such as concolor toxin (Mackessy & Castoe, 2016). See Table 1.

Feldner and colleagues (2016a, p. 65) recently point out another area of concern regarding work on venom and its variability in the Grand Canyon Rattlesnake and relatives:

Studies of *C. abyssus* venom generally do not provide specific capture data (Mackessy, 2010; Da Silva et al., 2011, 2012) and venom collected from snakes of known origin (Young & Miller, 1980) were acquired considerably downriver and on the opposite side of the Colorado River of our sampling locations. Sampled *abyssus* were from the A2 clade while snakes from the traditional range of *abyssus*, the likely origin of *abyssus* in venom studies, are in the A1 clade (Douglas et al., 2002; M. E. Douglas and G. Schuett, unpubl. data). The finding of a neurotoxin in adult snakes possessing *C. abyssus* haplotypes and morphology provides impetus for many questions such as: Are we seeing contact and exchange of genetic material? Is it a one-way transfer? Is it current or historical? How far down river does *C. abyssus* possess a *concolor*-like toxin and how far up into Utah? Does it only exist on the opposite side of the river where populations of *C. concolor* occur or does it occur in untested populations distant to *C. concolor*? And, is the neurotoxin derived from *C. concolor* or an independently-evolved character of *C. abyssus*?

Clearly, more field and laboratory work will be required before we have a definitive understanding of venom variability in Grand Canyon Rattlesnakes.

Similar looking species

In or near the Grand Canyon, identification of adult Grand Canyon Rattlesnakes is generally not problematic. Overall, the only species it might be confused with are light-colored (tan to tan-pink) individuals of the Prairie Rattlesnake (*Crotalus viridis*), and at the extreme eastern part of the canyon near Page, the closely relat-

Table 1

General distribution and venom toxicity of rattlesnakes of Arizona.

Species	General distribution[a]	VT (LD$_{50}$, μg/g)[b,c]	Type[b]
Crotalus atrox	S half Arizona	3.5	I
Crotalus cerastes	SW Arizona	2.4	I
Crotalus lepidus	SE Arizona (Sky Islands)	1.6	I*
Crotalus pyrrhus	C and W Arizona	2.5	I
Crotalus molossus	C and S Arizona	2.7	I
Crotalus abyssus	Grand Canyon and area	2.1	I
Crotalus cerberus	Central Arizona	5.4	I
Crotalus concolor	Extreme NE Arizona	0.4	II
Crotalus lutosus	Extreme NW Arizona	2.9	I
Crotalus pricei	SE AZ (Sky Islands)	1.3	I
Crotalus scutulatus	W and S Arizona	0.2	II (A)*
Crotalus tigris	South-central Arizona	0.07	II
Crotalus viridis	Extreme SW New Mexico	1.6	I
Crotalus viridis	NE Arizona	1.3	I
Crotalus willardi	SE AZ (Sky Islands)	4.2	I
Sistrurus tergeminus	Ext. SE AZ grasslands	1.4	I

[a] based on individual species' accounts. [b] Mackessy (2008, 2010). [c] Gibbs & Mackessy (2009). *Some populations show an opposite venom type. VT = venom toxicity. Modified from Mackessy & Castoe (2016).

An adult Grand Canyon Rattlesnake. Note that its color pattern shows signs of fading. Photo by M. Feldner.

ed Midget Faded Rattlesnake (*Crotalus concolor*). To a large extent, in this region, exact identification of rattlesnakes of the Western Group is not possible without precise locality information.

Neonates and juveniles of the Western Group are all similar in appearance and identification is confusing. In Arizona this includes the Grand Canyon Rattlesnake (*Crotalus abyssus*), Arizona Black Rattlesnake (*Crotalus cerberus*), Midget Faded Rattlesnake (*Crotalus concolor*), and Great Basin Rattlesnake (*Crotalus lutosus*). The closely related Prairie Rattlesnake (*Crotalus viridis*), sister to the Western Group, also is similar in appearance (see relationships of these species on page 21).

To make matters a bit more complicated, all of these species are capable of hybridization when they come into contact in nature (Klauber, 1972). However, hybridization and hybrid zones are largely unstudied in rattlesnakes (but see Zancolli et al., 2016). Today, next-generation DNA-based methods, bioinformatic analyses, venomics, and new morphological approaches will undoubtedly provide insights and advances to our understanding of the complexities of hybridization and hybrid zones of rattlesnakes (Davis, 2012; Schield et al., 2016; Zancolli et al., 2016).

Similar situations concerning identification and hybridization arise for all types of organisms, including birds (e.g., ducks and geese, Anseriformes), salamanders (e.g., genera *Ambystoma* and *Plethodon*), and frogs (e.g., genus *Rana*). For a comprehensive review on hybridization of birds, see Grant & Grant (1992).

Neonate rattlesnakes of the western group. (a) *C. abyssus*. (b) *C. cerberus*. (c) *C. concolor*. (d) *C. lutosus*. Photos (a) and (b) by M. Feldner, (c) L. Porras, and (d) B. O'Connor.

DISTRIBUTION & HABITATS

The specimen Laurence Klauber designated as the type for the Grand Canyon Rattlesnake (San Diego Natural History Museum, specimen number 02216) is from below the South Rim of the Grand Canyon, collected from Tanner Trail.

Since its original description, the Grand Canyon Rattlesnake was thought to be restricted to the Grand Canyon by most biologists. Recently, Feldner and colleagues (2016a, p. 77) emphasize this point:

Miller et al. (1982) stated *abyssus* was common at Diamond Creek and portrayed the range to extend as far west as Lake Mead, considerably west of any known specimens and undoubtedly due to the misidentification of *Crotalus pyrrhus*… Douglas et al. (2002) extended the range outside of the Grand Canyon and north into Utah. Campbell and Lamar (2004) reflect the findings of Douglas et al., Stebbins (2003) does not, and Brennan and Holycross (2006) state *C. abyssus* is "found exclusively within the Grand Canyon or a few miles of its rim".

However, recent work has altered this view, and the geographic range of the Grand Canyon Rattlesnake has become more extensive and complicated (reviewed by Feldner et al., 2016a). Michael Douglas and colleagues provided the first compelling evidence that the Grand Canyon Rattlesnake occurs outside the boundaries of the Grand Canyon proper, ranging north into southern Utah. According to their analysis, this species inhabits the canyon and cliff country of Coconino and Mohave counties (Arizona) associated with the Colorado River, but also in Kane and Garfield counties in southern Utah, between the Paria and Escalante rivers.

From the western area of its range, the Grand Canyon Rattlesnake occupies the Grand Canyon proper from National Canyon on the south side of the Colorado River at river mile 166.5 and on the north side of the river at Tuckup Canyon at river mile 164.5 (note: when specific river mileage is given, measurements begin at Lee's Ferry and increase moving to the west).

In the eastern area of its range, populations occur along the Grand Canyon and Colorado River, with individuals located on the south side of the river to river mile 47, but populations likely occur further east into Marble Canyon (Douglas et al., 2002). In the area of Page, Arizona the Grand Canyon Rattlesnake becomes scarce; the Midget Faded Rattlesnake (*Crotalus concolor*) becomes the dominant species based on DNA (mtDNA haplotype) sequence data recovered

Home of the Grand Canyon Rattlesnake. North Rim of GRCA near Red Rock Canyon. Photo by M. Feldner.

| Grand Canyon Rattlesnake, *Crotalus abyssus*

from multiple individuals that have been sampled (see Midget Faded Rattle-snake account).

On the north side of the Colorado River, the Grand Canyon Rattlesnake con-tinues into Utah to the vicinity of Rock Creek southwest of Fifty Mile Mountain, Kane County, Utah. It is not known how far the Grand Canyon Rattlesnake fol-lows the Colorado along its northern bank into Utah, but it is likely to be in the vicinity of the confluence of the Colorado River and Escalante River, ~68 miles (109.4 km) north of Lee's Ferry, or possibly as far as the Water Pocket Fold a few miles further upriver (Feldner et al., 2016a).

ECOLOGY & BEHAVIOR

Despite its iconic status, few ecological studies have been conducted on the Grand Canyon Rattlesnake. In the late 1990s, two researchers, Robert N. Reed and Michael E. Douglas, investigated the spatial activities and behavior of 13 adult Grand Canyon Rattlesnakes in Walter Powell Canyon, including a 4 km dis-tance (linear stretch) of the Little Colorado River Canyon (see Reed & Douglas, 2002).

Nine of 13 adult snakes were equipped with miniature radio-transmit-ters, which were surgically implanted into their body cavities. Radio-tracking showed that, on average, snakes moved 45 m (~148 feet) per movement and 26 m (~85 feet) per day. As expected, males moved longer distances than females, but movement frequency was not significantly different between sexes. Grand Canyon Rattlesnakes exhibited low directionality in their movements, unlike the spatial behavior of a closely related species, the Prairie Rattlesnake (*Crotalus viridis*), studied in Wyoming. The activity (home range) of the 9 Grand Canyon Rattlesnakes studied was from less than 4 hectares (~10 acres) to greater than 30 hectares (~74 acres). The corridor-like nature of the canyon bottom resulted in "forced" activity ranges that were elongated.

At this point in time, there are no published ecological studies of the Grand Canyon Rattlesnake in Utah.

POPULATION STATUS & CONSERVATION

By virtue of its presence in the Grand Canyon National Park, the Grand Canyon Rattlesnake gains protection from development and large-scale human perse-cution in Arizona. Study of populations in the GRCA is only by permission and time-sensitive scientific permits issued only to qualified individuals.

Construction of the Glen Canyon Dam, a 710-foot concrete structure on the Colorado River near the town of Page (Arizona), was completed in 1966 and forms Lake Powell. The Glen Canyon Dam provided subsequent stabilization of river flow which has resulted in more physical space between the shoreline of the river and desertscrub divisions of river corridor habitat.

Over the past 50 years, the riparian zone of the Grand Canyon has become wider and has resulted in an increase in plant diversity (including invasive species), insects, lizards, small mammals, birds, and other species. The Grand Canyon Rattlesnake likely has benefited from these changes by way of: i) the increased riparian habitat, and ii) increases in lizard and small rodent populations for prey. Despite these so-called positive effects on some populations, the Glen Canyon Dam is a contentious issue among environmentalists, who seek its removal.

Perhaps the greatest immediate threat to the Grand Canyon Rattlesnake is climate change. Recent modeling work on other species of rattlesnakes (e.g., *Crotalus cerberus*) of the Colorado Plateau has shown that this region is extremely vulnerable to climate change and wildfires. Other regions of the United States, particularly the Southwest, are vulnerable to similar kinds of impacts, but also human expansion, with accompanying degradation of habitat (e.g., highways, agriculture).

The Arizona Game and Fish Department (AZ G&F, 2014) provides a global and state rank that are essentially equal, and therein the Grand Canyon Rattlesnake (*Crotalus abyssus*) is described as secure, and apparently not vulnerable, within its range in Arizona. Utah does not yet recognize the presence of the Grand Canyon Rattlesnake within its borders in Utah, Administrative Code R657 53-28: Classification and Specific Rules for Reptiles (UT DWR, 2014). However, all species of rattlesnakes are protected in Utah and none can be removed without a proper license.

An adult Grand Canyon Rattlesnake eating a large Desert Spiny Lizard (*Sceloporus magister*). Photo by K. Haas.

Two adult male Grand Canyon Rattlesnakes in a ritualized fight, generally for priority of access to mates. Photo by N. Lehnberg.

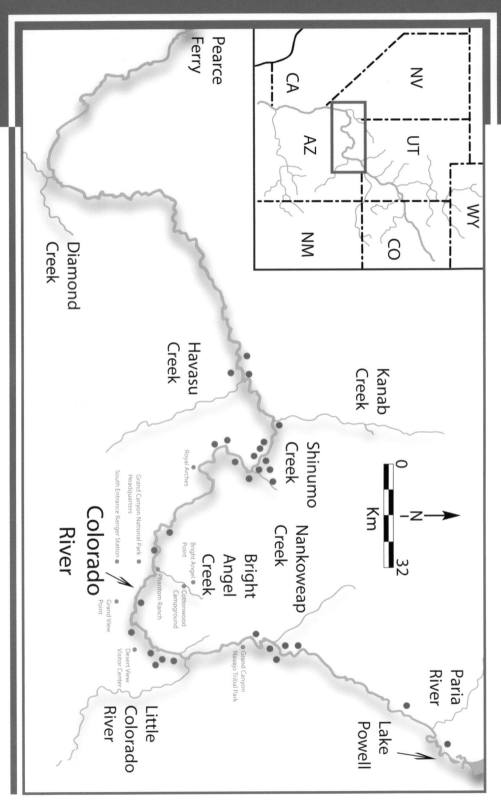

Map 1 (opposite page)

Distribution of the Grand Canyon Rattlesnake (*Crotalus abyssus*) within the GRCA. The red dots signify known sites, but are not exhaustive. For more information on *C. abyssus* see Douglas et al. (2002) and Feldner et al. (2016a).

Midget Faded Rattlesnake

Crotalus concolor

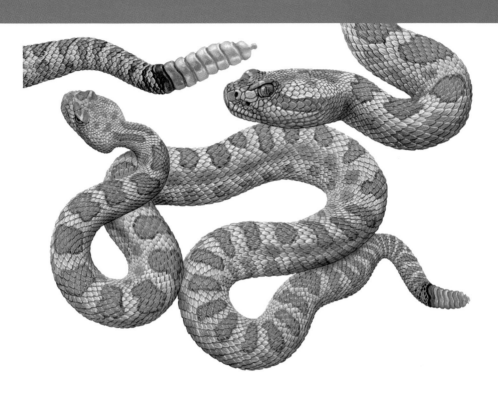

COMMON NAMES

The most widely accepted common name for this species is Midget Faded Rattlesnake. Reptile expert Laurence Klauber coined the name Midget Faded Rattlesnake nearly 90 years ago (Klauber, 1930). Other names that have been used and published in the literature include Midget-faded Rattlesnake, Midget Rattlesnake, Dwarf Rattlesnake, White Rattlesnake, and Yellow Rattlesnake.

SCIENTIFIC NAMES

The scientific name of the Midget Faded Rattlesnake has undergone change with increasing study and analysis (reviewed by Feldner et al., 2016b). Ironically, it was originally named *Crotalus concolor* by the University of California–Berkeley trained biologist Angus M. Woodbury, and that is the name used today by most biologists. This position is supported both by morphological and DNA-based evidence (Davis et al., 2016a). The genus name *Crotalus* comes from the Greek krotalon, which translates to rattle, castanet, or clapper. The species name *concolor*

is Latin and its translation means to be uniformly colored; the American Mountain Lion or Cougar bears the identical specific epithet for similar reasons (*Puma concolor*).

As mentioned earlier, scientific names of all organisms are best viewed as hypotheses that are (and should be) constantly challenged and tested by biologists.

DESCRIPTION

Body size

Adults of the Midget Faded Rattlesnake are small to medium sized snakes, and most attain a total length of no longer than 700 mm (including the rattle), or about 28 inches (Klauber, 1972; Feldner et al., 2016b). Individuals rarely exceed this size. As in most rattlesnakes, males can attain a slightly greater size (length and girth) than females.

All species of rattlesnakes are viviparous, or have live-birth. Midget Faded Rattlesnakes have small litters, ranging from 1–8 offspring. The mean (average) total length of newborns is 250 mm, which is similar to other members of the Western Rattlesnake complex (see accounts presented in Schuett et al., 2016). The smallest pregnant female was 522 mm (20.5 inches) in total length. Sexual maturity in males is likely at a similar size. Age at sexual maturity varies on ecological conditions (e.g., temperature, food availability) and a host of other factors (e.g., genetics), but in general both sexes attain reproductive competence in 3 to 4 years.

Pattern & coloration

Overall, adults of the Midget Faded Rattlesnake from various parts of their restricted range are similar in appearance. Typical of most members of the Western Rattlesnake group, neonates and juveniles of the Midget Faded Rattlesnake have well-defined dark blotches on a light (silver-gray) ground color. As they mature, the pattern fades to various degrees, often to the extent where the pattern becomes mostly obscure and resembles the ground color (Klauber, 1930, 1972).

An adult Midget Faded Rattlesnake with retained juvenile color pattern. Wayne County, Utah. Photo by L. Porras.

In adults the ground color is variable and can be straw, cream, yellow, tan, pale-brown, yellow-brown, reddish brown to various hues of red, orange, and (rarely) pink. In Arizona, the most common ground colors are tan, tan-brown, reddish-brown, and pink-orange (Feldner et al., 2016b). However, strict reliance on color and pattern alone as tools for identification in this species and other members of the Western Rattlesnake group is problematic and may lead to mis-identification (see below, *Similar looking species*).

The eye stripe (see image below) of the Midget Faded Rattlesnake typically passes horizontally above the posterior line of the mouth, remaining above and not encroaching on the supralabials, and sometimes ends approximately in line with the corner of the mouth (Feldner et al., 2016b).

An adult male Midget Faded Rattlesnake from Face Canyon, Coconino County, Arizona. Photo by M. Feldner.

Venom

Various studies have been conducted on the venom of the Western Group of rattlesnakes and close relatives (reviewed by Mackessy & Castoe, 2016). Some aspects of this work (e.g., toxicity) are summarized in Table 1 of this book (see page 32).

The venom of the Midget Faded Rattlesnake shows low metalloproteinase (protease enzyme) activity and but high toxicity (LD_{50}), attributable to the presence of an extremely potent presynaptic neurotoxin (aptly named concolor toxin) and myotoxins (Mackessy, 2010). Recent work in Stephen Mackessy's laboratory indicates that high metalloproteinase activity is incongruent (incompatible) with high toxicity neurotoxins, such as concolor toxin (Mackessy, 2010). In fact, of all the species in the Western Group, the Midget Faded Rattlesnake has the highest toxicity (lowest LD_{50}). Fortunate for us, bites to humans are exceedingly rare, primarily owing to the fact that Midget Faded Rattlesnake populations occur mostly in wilderness terrain and that they tend to be very docile (Feldner et al., 2016b).

Clearly, more field and laboratory work will be required before we have a definitive understanding of venom variability in the Western Rattlesnake group.

Similar looking species

Neonates and juveniles of the Western Group are all similar in appearance and identification is confusing. In Arizona this includes the Grand Canyon Rattlesnake (*Crotalus abyssus*), Arizona Black Rattlesnake (*Crotalus cerberus*), Midget Faded Rattlesnake (*Crotalus concolor*), and Great Basin Rattlesnake (*Crotalus lutosus*). The closely related Prairie Rattlesnake (*Crotalus viridis*), sister to the Western Group, also is similar in appearance (see relationships of these species on page 21).

To make matters a bit more complicated, all of these species are capable of hybridization when they come into contact in nature (Klauber, 1972). However, hybridization and hybrid zones are largely unstudied in rattlesnakes (but see Zancolli et al., 2016). Today, next-generation DNA-based methods, bioinformatic analyses, venomics, and new morphological approaches will undoubtedly provide insights and advances to our understanding of the complexities of hybridization and hybrid zones of rattlesnakes (Davis et al., 2016a; Schield et al., 2016; Zancolli et al., 2016).

DISTRIBUTION & HABITATS

The Midget Faded Rattlesnake is closely associated with river-carved canyon habitats created by the Green and Colorado rivers, *C. concolor* covers over 300 miles (483 km) of latitude from as far north as Sweetwater County in southwestern Wyoming in the Green River drainage, to Coconino County, Arizona in the south along the Colorado River.

The Midget Faded Rattlesnake has a limited distribution in Arizona; it is primarily known from the area of Page, where it is the predominant rattlesnake species.

ECOLOGY & BEHAVIOR

Several ecological studies have been conducted on the Midget Faded Rattlesnake, but all research thus far published has been restricted to southwestern Wyoming (Flaming Gorge National Recreation Area, Sweetwater County).

Kyle Ashton and Tim Patton (Ashton & Patton, 2001) studied three populations of the Midget Faded Rattlesnake in Wyoming to obtain data on reproduction and spatial ecology of pregnant females. Pregnant females emerged from den sites and made short distance movements to gestation and birthing rookeries. Thereafter, pregnant females made few movements during the remainder of gestation. Also, they did not hunt for food. Litters were produced from 20 August and 18 September. Mean litter size was 4.7 and was significantly related to female snout–vent length. Average offspring snout-vent length was 193 mm and average mass was 8.0 g. Reproduction in females appears to be biennial (every other year) or greater.

Ashton (Ashton, 2003) also conducted radio-telemetry research on the spatial ecology of male Midget Faded Rattlesnakes. Overall, males made short, infrequent movements. They moved an average of 2 ± 8 times during monitoring. Total distance traveled ranged from 0–876 m (median = 96 ± 326 m) and distance per movement averaged 45 ± 26 m. There was no evidence of migratory behavior or shifts in areas used during the monitoring period (May through September 1997, and May through July 1998). Mating behavior was only documented from 5–17 July 1997; mating behavior was not exhibited for the remainder of the monitoring period (18 July to 19 September). Males located and courted pre-shed females; successful copulation occurred between a pair that had recently shed. One instance of male-male combat was documented; as expected, the larger male displaced the smaller individual.

Joshua Parker and Stanley Anderson (Parker & Anderson, 2007) conducted a three-year ecological study of the Midget Faded Rattlesnake in the same area as Ashton (2003). They observed mating behavior from 21 July to 12 August. Females gave birth during the third week of August, and mean litter size was 4.17 offspring (range = 2–7).

At the time of this writing (June, 2018), there are no published ecological studies of the Midget Faded Rattlesnake in Arizona, Colorado, or Utah.

POPULATION STATUS & CONSERVATION

Populations of the Midget Faded Rattlesnake throughout its range (Wyoming, Utah, Colorado, and Arizona) occur mostly in wilderness terrain, much of it protected lands, and outside the direct influence of human development and similar disturbance.

This species is listed as State Special Concern by Colorado and is among the reptiles that are not allowed to be collected unless by special permit (Colorado Parks and Wildlife, 2014). Under R657-53-28, Classification and Specific Rules for Reptiles, collection or possession of Midget Faded Rattlesnakes is prohibited in Utah. Under Section 11 of Chapter 52 of the Wyoming Game & Fish Commission collection of Midget Faded Rattlesnakes is not allowed because it is considered a Species of Management Concern. Currently, the Midget Faded Rattlesnake can be legally collected in Arizona using a non-game hunting license.

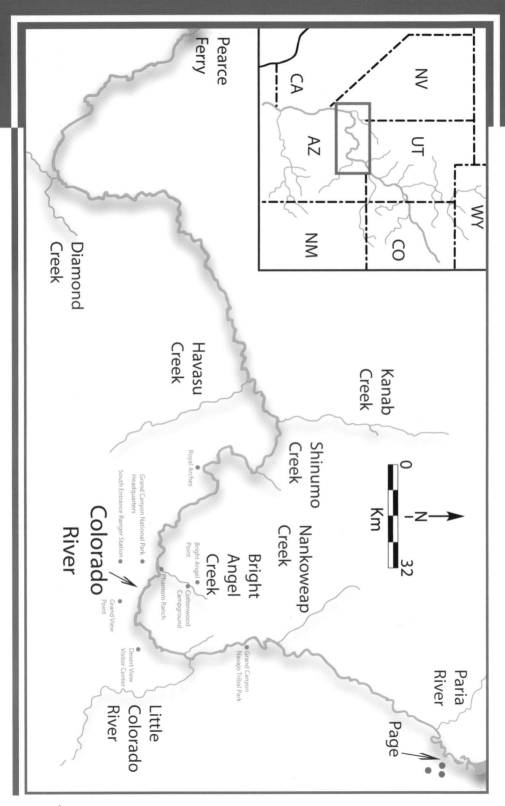

| Midget Faded Rattlesnake, *Crotalus concolor*

Map 2 (opposite page)

Distribution of the Midget Faded Rattlesnake (*Crotalus concolor*) at the eastern-most area of the GRCA. The red dots signify known sites near Page. For more information on *C. concolor* see Douglas et al. (2002) and Feldner et al. (2016b).

Great Basin Rattlesnake

Crotalus lutosus

COMMON NAMES

The name Great Basin Rattlesnake was coined by Klauber (1930) as the common name for this species in his original description (Klauber, 1930). The specific epithet refers to "muddy," which is interpreted to denote the ground coloration of adult snakes. That name remains the accepted vernacular or common name today; no other common name is regularly used for this taxon.

SCIENTIFIC NAMES

Like other members of the Western Group, the scientific name of the Great Basin Rattlesnake has undergone change with increasing study and analysis. The original binomial name designated by Klauber in 1930 was *Crotalus confluentus lutosus* (Klauber, 1930). Several years later Klauber himself reassigned the name as a subspecies of the Prairie Rattlesnake, *Crotalus viridis lutosus* (Klauber, 1936).

The specimen Laurence Klauber designated as the holotype for the Great Basin Rattlesnake is from near Abram, Utah (Millard County) (Specimen deposited in the San Diego Natural History Museum).

Decades later, in the 1990s, researchers using mitochondrial DNA sequence evidence designated the Great Basin Rattlesnake (*Crotalus viridis lutosus*) as a subspecies of the Western Rattlesnake, *Crotalus oreganus lutosus* (see Pook et al., 2000; Ashton & de Queiroz, 2001). Currently, owing to additional evidence from DNA sequence data and modern morphological analyses, the Great Basin Rattlesnake is recognized as a full species, and its binomial name has been adjusted to *Crotalus lutosus* (see Douglas et al., 2002; Davis, 2016).

An adult Great Basin Rattlesnake from Coconino County, Arizona. Photo by B. Hughes.

DESCRIPTION
Body size
The Great Basin Rattlesnake is one of the largest members of the Western Group; older adults can be medium- to large-sized snakes, sometimes exceeding a total length of 1200 mm, or about 4 feet (Feldner et al., 2016c). As mentioned, sexual size dimorphism (SSD) is a common phenomenon in rattlesnakes, with males typically attaining greater sizes (total length) than females, which is the situation in the Great Basin Rattlesnake (Klauber, 1972).

There is geographic variability in body size. Individuals from the Anaho Island in Pyramid Lake in Nevada, for example, show size reduction compared to individuals found on the nearby mainland. In many species with large geographic distributions, such as in the Great Basin Rattlesnake, body size variation is commonplace. The Western Diamond-backed Rattlesnake (*Crotalus atrox*), which has one of the most extensive geographic distributions among rattlesnakes, shows wide variation in body size, even within one state, Arizona (Amarello et al., 2010). Size differences, which may be heritable, are likely due to habitat quality, differing prey densities, temperatures, rainfall (moisture), conditions that shorten the active season, local adaptation, and possibly competition with other predators, including other species of snakes (Amarello et al., 2010; Feldner et al., 2016a).

The mean (average) total length of neonates is 265 mm, which is similar to other members of the Western Rattlesnake complex (see Davis, 2016). The smallest pregnant female was 557 mm in total length, and sexual maturity in males is likely at a similar size.

Pattern, coloration, & scalation

Typical of all members of the Western Rattlesnake group, neonates and juveniles of the Great Basin Rattlesnake have dark, contrasting blotches on a light gray or tan background. Blotches typically darken with age, but in some cases the pattern fades (Klauber, 1930, 1972).

A juvenile Great Basin Rattlesnake from Coconino County, Arizona. Photo by E. Cassano.

In adults the ground color is yellow, yellow-brown, grayish, or pinkish (Klauber, 1930; Feldner et al., 2016c). The coloration of individuals from Arizona varies greatly; commonly individuals have subtle pastels of orange, pink, and taupe suffusing the background coloration which may be pale or dark (Feldner et al., 2016c). A pregnant female in captivity was observed to undergo color change, from a light taupe-gray to a darker ruddy-gray (J. Slone and M. Feldner, pers. comm.).

An adult Great Basin Rattlesnake from near Deer Creek, GRCA. Photo by M. Feldner.

There are 32–49 (mean = 40) brown to black dorsal markings (blotches) with light centers; they often have serrated or irregular edges. The main body blotches are of various shapes and sometimes faded with only the blotch border evident, or they can be uniformly black and not bordered by scales lighter than ground color.

Interestingly, in some areas of Nevada, the Great Basin Rattlesnake shows black and white tail bands, a character seen in other species such as the *atrox* group (e.g., *Crotalus atrox, C. ruber*, and others). In the Grand Canyon and nearby areas, individuals of the Southwestern Speckled Rattlesnake (*Crotalus pyrrhus*) often show black and white tail bands. But, for the Great Basin Rattlesnake, this character deviates from the typical condition in which the tail and tail bands match the ground color (Blake Thomason, unpublished data; see Feldner et al., 2016c) (see image on following page).

Dark pigment is present on the head of many adults of the Great Basin Rattlesnake, which is typically not present in the Grand Canyon Rattlesnake and Midget Faded Rattlesnake.

Venom

Since its description in 1930, various studies have been conducted on the venom of the Great Basin Rattlesnake and its close relatives (see relationships of the species on page 21). Some of this work was aimed to better understand relationships to other members of the Western Rattlesnake group.

The venom of the Great Basin Rattlesnake (*Crotalus lutosus*) has been shown to be similar to venom of the Grand Canyon Rattlesnake (*Crotalus abyssus*). See Table 1 in this book (page 32). First to demonstrate these similarities was R. A. Young and colleagues. Young & Miller (1980) determined that the venom of the Great Basin Rattlesnake was more similar to the venom of the Grand Canyon Rattlesnake, compared to the venoms of the Prairie (Hopi) Rattlesnake (*Crotalus viridis nuntius*) and Midget Faded Rattlesnake (*Crotalus concolor*). They determined that the Great Basin Rattlesnake shares 11 of 18 protein fractions with the Grand Canyon Rattlesnake, and only 9 protein fractions with the Prairie (Hopi) Rattlesnake and Midget Faded Rattlesnake.

More recently, Stephen Mackessy and his laboratory have shown that both the Great Basin Rattlesnake and Grand Canyon Rattlesnake have high metalloproteinase activity and are considerably lower in toxicity (LD_{50}) than another close (sister group) relative, the Midget Faded Rattlesnake (*Crotalus concolor*), which has potent neurotoxins (concolor toxin) and myotoxins (Mackessy et al., 2003). Recent work in Stephen Mackessy's lab shows that high metalloproteinase activity is incongruent (incompatible) with high toxicity neurotoxins, such as concolor toxin (Mackessy, 2010; see Mackessy & Castoe, 2016).

Clearly, more field and laboratory work will be required before we have a definitive understanding of venom variability in the Great Basin Rattlesnake.

Similar looking species

Throughout most of its range, the Great Basin is the only species of rattlesnake present, thus eliminating confusion with respect to its identification

Adult *Crotalus viridis* from northern Arizona. (a) Hopi Rattlesnake (*C. v. nuntius*) from an area near Winslow. Photo by W. Wells. (b) Hopi Rattlesnake (*C. v. nuntius*) from an area near Red Butte, Coconino County. Photo by D. DeNardo.

in the field. Identification of adult Great Basin Rattlesnakes within the Grand Canyon is generally not problematic, and the only species it might be confused with are adults of the Grand Canyon Rattlesnake (*Crotalus abyssus*) and Prairie Rattlesnake (*Crotalus viridis*). It tends to be distinct in appearance from the closely related Midget Faded Rattlesnake (*Crotalus concolor*). However, as mentioned earlier, exact identification of rattlesnakes of the Western Group is not possible without precise locality information.

Neonates and juveniles of the Western Group are all similar in appearance, and identification is confusing. In Arizona this includes the Grand Canyon Rattlesnake (*Crotalus abyssus*), Arizona Black Rattlesnake (*Crotalus cerberus*), Midget Faded Rattlesnake (*Crotalus concolor*), and Great Basin Rattlesnake (*Crotalus lutosus*). The closely related Prairie Rattlesnake (*Crotalus viridis*), sister to the Western Group, also is similar in appearance (see relationships of these species on page 21). It is not likely to be confused with other species in its range, such as the Southwestern Speckled Rattlesnake (*Crotalus pyrrhus*).

As mentioned above, all of these species are capable of hybridization when they come into contact in nature (Klauber, 1972). However, hybridization and hybrid zones are largely unstudied in rattlesnakes (but see Zancolli et al., 2016).

DISTRIBUTION & HABITATS

The Great Basin Rattlesnake has one of the most extensive geographic distributions of any member of the Western Group, which spans most of the region termed the Great Basin. It occurs in 6 states, specifically western Utah, most of Nevada, northwestern California, southern Idaho, southeastern Oregon, and extreme northwestern Arizona, including the region coined "Arizona Strip" and the Grand Canyon itself.

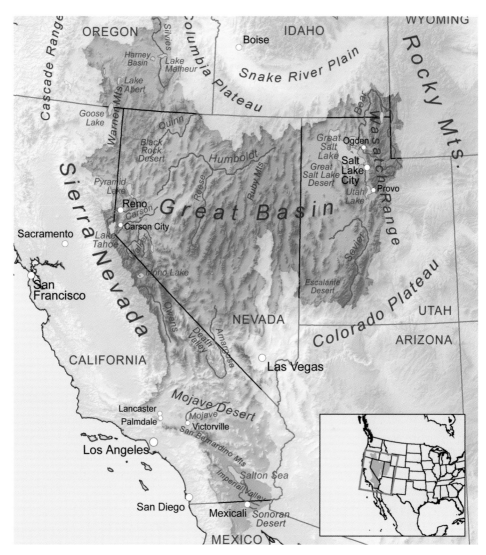

U.S. map highlighting the region defined as the Great Basin, which primarily encompasses Nevada and Utah, but also includes parts of California, Idaho, Oregon, and Wyoming.

In Arizona, the Great Basin Rattlesnake is present in Mohave and Coconino counties (see habitat image on page 60). It occurs in an area approximated by the Virgin Mountains in northwest Arizona, south to Snap Point on the North Rim of the Grand Canyon, to the eastern flank of the Kaibab Plateau and House Rock Valley to below Paria Point, down to the level of the Colorado River on both the west and east side of the Kaibab Plateau at multiple locations between South and Tuckup Canyons, and north to the Utah border (Douglas et al., 2002; Feldner et al., 2016c). Great Basin Rattlesnakes can be found at widely varying elevations, from 549 m at Tuckup Canyon on the Colorado River to at least 2438 m in other parts of its range (Feldner et al., 2016c).

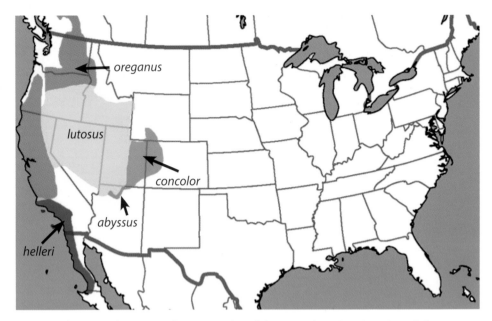

U.S. map depicting the geographic range of 5 of the 6 species of rattlesnakes of the western group. *Crotalus cerberus* is not included (central Arizona and extreme western New Mexico).

Detailed information on the distribution of the Great Basin Rattlesnake in Arizona, the Grand Canyon and nearby regions, and throughout its extensive range has been detailed by Feldner and colleagues (Feldner et al., 2016c).

ECOLOGY & BEHAVIOR

Most ecological studies of the Western Group have involved the Great Basin Rattlesnake, and extensive study has focused on populations in northern Utah, southern Idaho, and Nevada. At this point in time, there are no published ecological studies of the Great Basin Rattlesnake in Arizona.

Among the first studies, William S. Parker and William S. Brown investigated den use in the Great Basin Rattlesnake and other species of snakes near the eastern foothills of the Stansbury Mountains of Utah (Parker & Brown, 1973). In this study, various parameters were investigated including species present and estimations of the total biomass of snakes at the dens. They mentioned that space for denning is apparently not a factor controlling maximum snake population densities at this locality.

Lowell V. Diller and Richard L. Wallace studied the ecology and behavior of the Great Basin Rattlesnakes in Idaho from 1975 to 1980 (Diller & Wallace, 1996). The parameters studied were (1) seasonal and daily activity patterns, (2) body temperatures, (3) habitat, and (4) food. Also, life-history traits were studied related to reproduction. Interestingly, Townsend's Ground Squirrel (*Spermophilus*

Habitat of the Great Basin Rattlesnake in northern Arizona. Navajo Trail Road, Colorado City near Hurricane Cliffs. Photo by W. Wells.

townsendii) comprised 80% of the prey hunted and consumed by the 454 rattlesnakes they sampled. Female Great Basin Rattlesnakes tends to reproduce (give birth) every other year (biennially) or less often in this population.

Recently, Xavier Glaudas and colleagues studied timing of reproduction in the Great Basin Rattlesnake in Nevada (Glaudas et al., 2009). In their study, they examined the reproductive tracts of 275 museum-preserved specimens of this species to investigate the reproductive strategies used by the only species of rattlesnake widely occurring in a cold desert, the Great Basin Desert. The smallest mature male and female examined were 50.8 cm and 51.4 cm snout-vent length, respectively. Most females reproduce every other year, thus a biennial cycle. Like other rattlesnakes, males have the potential for annual reproduction (see Taylor & Booth, 2016). Overall, their museum findings suggest that the relatively short active season (4–5 months) has important implications for the timing of female reproductive events, such as early onset of ova development (vitellogenesis), late timing of ovulation and fertilization, and possibly a restricted period for gestation and giving birth.

POPULATION STATUS & CONSERVATION

Throughout its extensive range in wilderness not occupied by humans, the Great Basin Rattlesnake enjoys protection by sheer isolation. And by virtue of its presence in the Grand Canyon National Park, it is protected from development and large-scale human persecution in Arizona. Research on populations in the

GRCA is only by permission, and time-sensitive scientific permits are issued only to qualified individuals.

Perhaps the greatest immediate threat to the Great Basin Rattlesnake is climate change. Recent modeling work on other species of rattlesnakes (e.g., *Crotalus cerberus*) of the Colorado Plateau has shown that this region is extremely vulnerable to climate change (increasing temperatures and extreme drought) and wildfires (Douglas et al., 2016).

The Arizona Game and Fish Department (AZ G&F, 2014) provides no special protection for the Great Basin Rattlesnake. The Arizona Game and Fish Department regulates the take of the Great Basin Rattlesnake through guidance of the Arizona Revised Statutes (Title 17) and Commission Order 43. To pursue, collect, or capture this species, a valid Arizona hunting license is required; holders of hunting licenses may collect up to four snakes in a year with the maximum number of snakes allowed in possession at any time being four snakes live or dead.

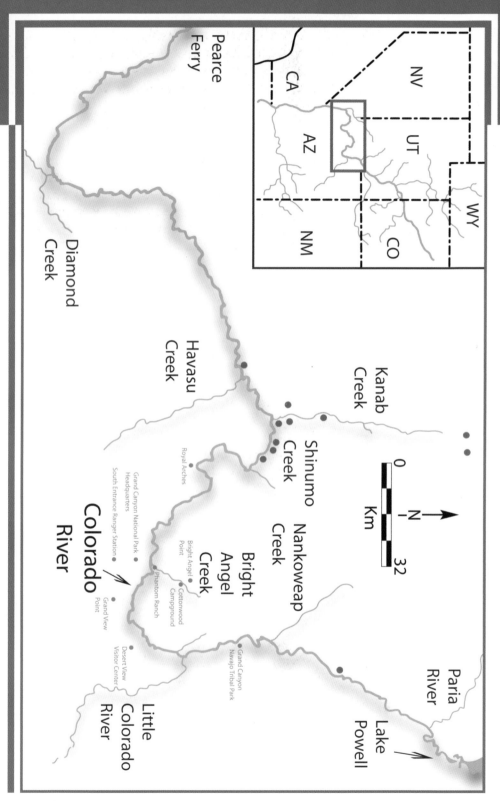

Map 3 (opposite page)

Distribution of the Great Basin Rattlesnake (*Crotalus lutosus*) within the GRCA. The red dots signify known sites, but are not exhaustive. For more information on *C. lutosus*, see Douglas et al. (2002) and Feldner et al. (2016c).

Prairie Rattlesnake
Crotalus viridis

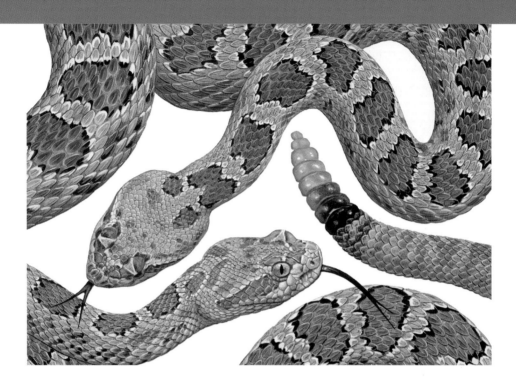

COMMON NAMES

Owing to the fact that it has such an extensive range in North America, the Prairie Rattlesnake has acquired several other names used locally, including the Western Rattlesnake and Spotted Rattlesnake (Klauber, 1972). Today the accepted vernacular or common name by the scientific community is Prairie Rattlesnake and two subspecies are recognized (Klauber, 1972). One of the two subspecies is endemic to the Painted Desert of northeastern Arizona; it is named the Hopi Rattlesnake (*Crotalus v. nuntius*). Like the Grand Canyon Rattlesnake, the Hopi Rattlesnake has sometimes been called the Pink or Orange Rattlesnake; individuals from the area of Meteor Crater (Coconino County, Arizona) or nearby often are dull pink or reddish-orange in coloration.

SCIENTIFIC NAMES

The scientific name of the Prairie Rattlesnake has undergone little change over the past 90 years, since Laurence Klauber worked with this group (Klauber, 1930, 1935). Nonetheless, there have been a few changes with increasing study and analysis. The original binomial name designated by Klauber (1930) was *Crotalus confluentus*. Several years later, Klauber reassigned the scientific name as *Crotalus viridis* (Klauber, 1935). The specific epithet *viridis* is Latin for green. Decades later, using mitochondrial DNA evidence, Hugh Quinn (1987) partitioned the *viridis* group into 2 primary clades: eastern (designated as *Crotalus viridis* and subspecies) and western (designated as *Crotalus oreganus* and subspecies). Currently, owing to additional evidence from DNA sequence data and modern morphological analyses, members of the western clade (Western Group) are largely recognized as full species (Douglas et al., 2002; Davis et al., 2016a; Schuett et al., 2016; Dreslik, 2017).

Two subspecies of the Prairie Rattlesnake are recognized (Klauber, 1935, 1936) and both are found in Arizona: the wide-ranging Prairie Rattlesnake (*Crotalus v. viridis*) (see image below) and the endemic Hopi Rattlesnake (*Crotalus v. nuntius*) (see image next page). The subspecific epithet *nuntius* is derived from Latin and its translation means "messenger."

DESCRIPTION
Body size
Adults of the Prairie Rattlesnake can be medium- to large-sized snakes; some individuals have attained total lengths of 1450 mm, or nearly 5 feet (Klauber, 1972; Davis & Douglas, 2016).

Sexual size dimorphism (SSD) is a common phenomenon in rattlesnakes, typically with males attaining greater sizes than females, which is the situation

An adult Prairie Rattlesnake (*Crotalus v. viridis*). Apache County, Arizona. Photo by R. Babb.

A juvenile Hopi Rattlesnake (*Crotalus v. nuntius*) from northern Arizona. Photo by W. Wells.

in both subspecies of the Prairie Rattlesnake (Klauber, 1972). It is clear, however, that there is extreme local variability in the overall adult size of this species, with some of the smallest individuals occurring in northeastern Arizona and eastern Utah [457-559 mm (18-22 inches) in total length] to the impressive leviathans hailing from in Montana (> 48 inches).

The mean (average) total length of newborns is 250 mm, which is similar to members of the Western Rattlesnake complex (Schuett et al., 2016). The smallest pregnant female measured 684 mm total length, and sexual maturity in males is likely a similar size.

Pattern & coloration
Similar to the Western Group, neonates and juveniles of the Prairie Rattlesnake display dark dorsal blotches on a pale green or light tan background. Depending on geographic location, there are from 20 to 57 dark blotches on the dorsum of the body; the dorsal blotches are often outlined in white and black (see following page).

With maturity at about 3 to 4-years-old, the ground color of some individuals undergoes a fairly dramatic change. In the Prairie Rattlesnake, the ground color of adults ranges from hues of green to tan, and in the Hopi Rattlesnake the ground color can be bright and range from salmon to reddish-orange, some times suffused with green. The ground color in some individuals of the Hopi Rattlesnakes is mostly hues of green.

Newborn Prairie Rattlesnakes from Arizona. (a) A Prairie Rattlesnake (*C. v. viridis*) from Apache County. Photo by R. Babb. (b) A Hopi Rattlesnake (*C. v. nuntius*) from Coconino County. Photo by B. O'Connor.

Venom

Numerous studies have been conducted on the venom of the Prairie Rattlesnake and its close relatives of the Western Group. Some of this work was aimed to better understand species relations. A small portion of this work is summarized in Table 1 on page 32.

Stephen Mackessy (2010) has investigated venoms of the Prairie Rattlesnake and members of the Western Group. Interestingly, he found moderate to high levels of seven common viperid venom enzymes common to *Crotalus viridis* and the other 8 taxa ("subspecies") that were sampled. But he did find several notable exceptions to any sort of absolute trend. Arizona Black Rattlesnakes (*Crotalus cerberus*), for example, have exceptionally high levels of metalloproteinase (enzyme) activity. Other species with high levels of this enzyme were *C. abyssus* and *C. lutosus*, and *C. viridis* was intermediate. Lethal toxicity [LD_{50} (mg/g)] toward inbred mice also was lowest in *C. cerberus*. On the other hand, Midget Faded Rattlesnakes (*Crotalus concolor*) have very low levels of metalloproteinase but high toxicity. Interestingly, *C. concolor* has a very potent pre-synaptic neurotoxin (concolor toxin). The venom of *C. viridis* (both subspecies) also has a high toxicity to mice.

Clearly, more field and laboratory work will be required before we have a definitive understanding of venom variability in the Prairie Rattlesnake and its close relatives of the Western Group (see Mackessy & Castoe, 2016).

Similar looking species

Neonates and juveniles of the Prairie Rattlesnake bear a striking similarity to members of the Western Group; in Arizona that includes the Grand Canyon Rattlesnake, Arizona Black Rattlesnake, Midget Faded Rattlesnake, and the Great Basin Rattlesnake. As both juveniles and adults, the Prairie Rattlesnake also can bear an uncanny resemblance to the Mojave Rattlesnake (*Crotalus scutulatus*), but that species is uncommon in the Grand Canyon (see review by Cardwell, 2016). This is likely more than pure coincidence owing to the fact that the Mojave Rattlesnake is sister to the Prairie Rattlesnake + Western Group.

Adult Prairie Rattlesnakes (*C. v. viridis*) tend to be distinctive and bear little resemblance to members of the Western Group. Furthermore, in many areas of its range, it is the only species of rattlesnake present. However, the Hopi Rattlesnake (*C. v. nuntius*) is sometimes mistaken for the Grand Canyon Rattlesnake in areas of the Grand Canyon where the two taxa occur near each other (sympatric) or (rarely) overlap.

Hybridization can make identification problematic in some areas of its range. In northern Arizona, hybridization between the Hopi Rattlesnake and Grand Canyon Rattlesnake is possible in the areas at or near the confluence of the Colorado and Little Colorado rivers of the Grand Canyon, and elsewhere (e.g., Bitter Springs, Arizona). In the bootheel region of extreme southwestern New Mexico and nearby Cochise County in extreme southeastern Arizona, hybrids between the Mojave Rattlesnake (*Crotalus scutulatus*) and

An adult Mojave Rattlesnake (*Crotalus scutulatus*) from Maricopa County, Arizona. Photo by W. Wells.

Hybrid rattlesnakes. (a) Juvenile *Crotalus scutulatus* x *C. v. viridis*. Hidalgo County, New Mexico. Photo by C. Smith. (b) Adult hybrid from the same locality as (a). Photo by W. Wüster.

the Prairie Rattlesnake (*Crotalus viridis*) are common; key work is by Giulia Zancolli, Wolfgang Wüster, and their colleagues (Zancolli et al., 2016). Examples of *C. scutulatus* x *C. viridis* hybrids from New Mexico are provided above.

DISTRIBUTION & HABITATS

The geographic range of the Prairie Rattlesnake is extensive, extending from extreme northeastern Sonora in northern Chihuahua and northwestern Coahuila (Mexico) through 11 western states (including extreme western Iowa), and reaches its northern-most limits in southwestern Saskatchewan and southeastern Alberta (Canada). The Prairie Rattlesnake (*C. v. viridis*) is primarily found in the northeastern region of Arizona (Apache, Navajo, and Coconino counties). The Hopi Rattlesnake has a more restricted distribution in Apache, Coconino, and Navajo counties. In their recent review, Davis & Douglas (2016, p. 289) state:

> More narrowly, the distribution of the Hopi Rattlesnake extends westward from the New Mexico border to U.S. Highway 66 in central Arizona, and is matched on all sides by the Prairie Rattlesnake.

Accordingly, the Hopi Rattlesnake occupies a good portion of the Painted Desert, and westward it is found along and below the South Rim of the Grand Canyon; it is also known to enter the Grand Canyon at various points (see Miller et al., 1982, p. 71).

Despite claims that the Prairie Rattlesnake occurs in southeastern Arizona (Cochise County), no voucher specimens are known. The species is found just to the east in the bootheel of New Mexico (Hidalgo County).

The Prairie Rattlesnake occupies a wide range of habitats throughout its extensive range, including Great Basin Desertscrub, Plains and Great Basin Grasslands, and Great Basin Conifer Woodland. See review by Davis & Douglas (2016).

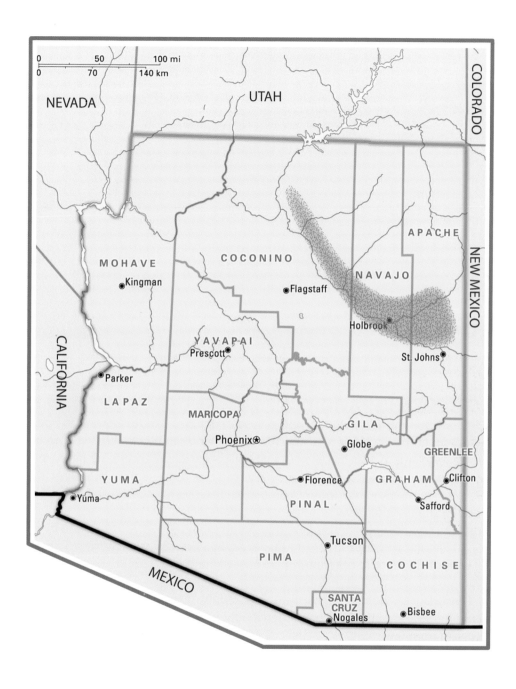

The Painted Desert is in the Four Corners region (AZ, CO, NM, and UT). It forms an arc that is 190 km (118 miles) in length and 97 km (60 miles) in width. It covers an area of 19,425 km² (7500 miles²). Modified from Encyclopedia Britannica, Inc. (1998).

Habitat of the Prairie Rattlesnake in northern Arizona. Painted Desert.

ECOLOGY & BEHAVIOR

There are numerous behavioral and ecological studies conducted on the nominate form of the Prairie Rattlesnake (*Crotalus v. viridis*). Among the first employing radio-telemetry was by David Duvall and colleagues (Duvall & Schuett, 1997; Duvall et al., 1990; King & Duvall, 1990), studying a population of Prairie Rattlesnakes in the Haystack Mountains, a cold-desert region of central Wyoming, north of the town of Rawlins. More recent work includes studies in eastern Colorado by Bryan Shipley and colleagues (Shipley et al., 2013), central Idaho by Javan M. Bauder and colleagues (Bauder et al., 2015), and Saskatchewan, Canada by Laura Gardiner and colleagues (Gardiner et al., 2016).

David Duvall, Gordon Schuett and colleagues (Duvall et al., 1992; Duvall & Schuett, 1997) investigated generalized mating systems parameters of Prairie Rattlesnake from Wyoming, with especial interest in male movements and mating success. Several of the specific ideas and questions they tested were as follows: (1) Do males seek females during a brief reproductive period? (2) Are females relatively few? (3) Are females widely and unpredictably distributed in small, discrete clusters? and (4) Do males show efficient mate-searching patterns? Overall, the major finding was that straight-line (i.e. fixed-bearing) movements by male Prairie Rattlesnakes was exhibited during mate-searching in summer. This type of movement pattern by males appears critical for location of mates when females are widely and unpredictably distributed into small, discrete clusters; it is associated with greater relative mating success.

In Prairie Rattlesnakes fitted with radio-transmitters, Bryan Shipley and colleagues (Shipley et al., 2016) have recently reported on winter "den" use of Black-tailed Prairie Dog (*Cynomys ludovicianus*) burrows in colonies within a short-grass prairie in Arapahoe County, Colorado. The rattlesnakes moved 0.7 times per day, traveling 89 meters (292 feet) per movement. Home range sizes varied from 0.3–31.4 hectares (0.74 -77.6 acres, respectively). All snakes showed fidelity to colony sites, returning in the fall to the same Prairie Dog colony in which they hibernated the previous winter.

In the Frank Church Wilderness in central Idaho, Javan M. Bauder and colleagues (Bauder et al., 2015) used radio-telemetry over several seasons to investigate the movement patterns of 21 male and 6 non-pregnant female Prairie Rattlesnakes (*Crotalus v. viridis*) in a mountainous landscape. The main objective was to compare this population to those of migratory populations from areas with lower topographic relief. Mean total distance moved during the entire activity season in one season was 4.46 km (range 1.38–7.67); mean maximum distance moved from the hibernaculum was 1.46 km (range 0.69–2.71). This suggests that Prairie Rattlesnakes are capable of making considerable movements in a mountainous landscape, similar to elsewhere in their range where topographic relief is relaxed.

At Grasslands National Park in Saskatchewan (Canada), Laura E. Gardiner and colleagues (Gardiner et al., 2015) used radio-telemetry to investigate habitat selection and use in Prairie Rattlesnakes. They found that Prairie Rattlesnakes selected specific sites (i.e., within 1 m) with shrub cover and burrows and avoided bare ground. Shrub cover was two-times higher at used sites compared to available ones, while bare ground showed the opposite trend. Roughly 66% all of rattlesnake location points were within 1 m of a burrow, which suggests that retreat sites are important survival and other factors.

POPULATION STATUS & CONSERVATION

By virtue of its presence in wilderness areas of most of Arizona, including the Grand Canyon National Park and other protected areas, the Prairie Rattlesnake and Hopi Rattlesnake gain protection from development and large-scale human persecution. Study of populations in the GRCA is only by permission, and time-sensitive scientific permits issued only to qualified individuals.

Perhaps the greatest immediate threat to some populations of *Crotalus viridis* is climate change and wildfires. Recent modeling work on other species of rattlesnakes (e.g., *Crotalus cerberus*) of the Colorado Plateau has shown that this region is extremely vulnerable to climate change and wildfires (Douglas et al., 2016). Other regions of the Southwest are vulnerable to similar kinds of impacts, but also human expansion, with accompanying degradation of habitat (e.g., highways, agriculture).

In Arizona, Prairie Rattlesnakes can be taken with a valid hunting license under Arizona Revised Statute 17331. There is no closed season (i.e., killed or collected anytime), per Arizona Game and Fish Commission Order 43(A) with a limit of four animals per year or in possession, dead or alive.

Prairie Rattlesnake (*Crotalus v. nuntius*). Artwork by Tell Hicks.

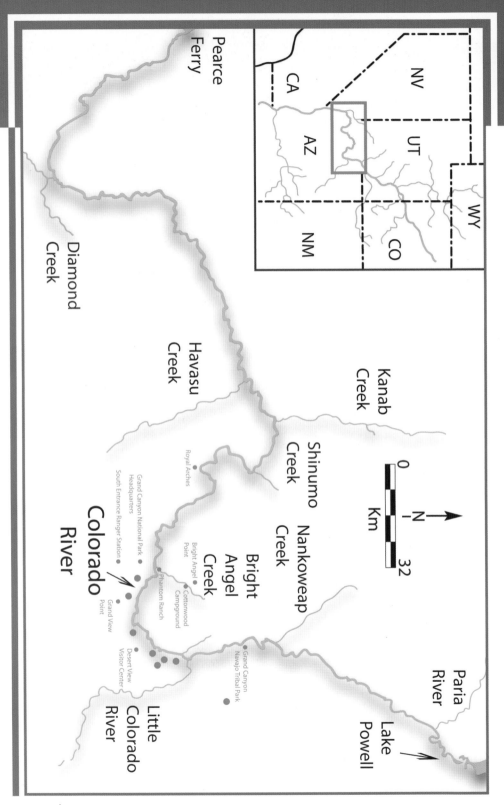

Map 4 (opposite page)

Distribution of the Prairie Rattlesnake (*Crotalus viridis*) within the GRCA. The red dots denote known sites, but are not exhaustive. For more information on *C. viridis* see Douglas et al. (2002) and Davis & Douglas (2016).

Western Diamond-backed Rattlesnake
Crotalus atrox

COMMON NAMES
The most widely accepted common name for this species is Western Diamond-backed Rattlesnake. Other common names are coontail and diamondback. Spanish names include vibora de cascabel and vibora serrana (Campbell and Lamar, 2004).

SCIENTIFIC NAMES
The original description does not describe the etymology of the specific epithet (Baird and Girard, 1853), but presumably *atrox* comes from the Latin root for "atrocious." The type locality (holotype USNM 7761, paratypes USM 7760, 255) is "Indianola", Calhoun County, Texas. The binomial *Crotalus cinereous* had priority over *Crotalus atrox*, but this name was suppressed by the ICZN and *C. atrox* is the accepted name (McDiarmid et al., 1999, referring to ICZN, 1955).

DESCRIPTION

Body size

With respect length and body mass, *Crotalus atrox* is indisputably the largest rattlesnake in Arizona (Lowe et al., 1986; Brennan and Holycross, 2006). It is the second largest rattlesnake in the United States, rivaled only by the Eastern Diamond-backed Rattlesnake, *Crotalus adamanteus* (Campbell and Lamar, 2004).

Melissa Amarello and team (Amarello et al., 2010) investigated geographical, environmental, and sex-related differences of body size in *C. atrox* from Arizona. In that study, the largest (SVL) individual measured was a male (1438 mm) from Cochise County. The largest individual female measured (1144 mm) also was from Cochise County. Males, on average, attain greater sizes (length and mass) than females, which is typical of other rattlesnake species (Klauber, 1972).

Pattern & coloration

The ground color of adult *C. atrox* is highly variable and largely corresponds to geographical location. Most common it is a dusty-looking grayish-brown, rarely black, but also greenish- and pinkish-brown, orange, pinkish, yellow-green or chalky white (Klauber, 1972). The dorsal ground color is overlaid with a series of 23–45 dark, light-bordered, diamond-shaped (or hexagonal blotches) that are present on the dorsum (excluding the tail).

The tail coloration is in sharp contrast to the body in color and pattern. The tail has two to eight (usually four to six) distinctive and wide black bands separated by white or ash white interspaces. This led to the nickname of "coon-tail," though other species of rattlesnakes have similarly banded tails but tend to be less distinctive. Newborns strongly resemble adults.

Western Diamond-backed Rattlesnake (*Crotalus atrox*). Central Arizona. Photo by W. Wells.

Venom

The venom of *C. atrox* is primarily hemotoxic and contains hemorrhagic (causing an escape of blood) components referred to as metalloproteinases. Cytotokins and myotoxins are also commonly present (Mackessy and Castoe, 2016). The metalloproteinases of *C. atrox* venom can induce ischemia (inadequate blood supply) in muscle tissue as a consequence of bleeding and reduced perfusion. The LD_{50} values (2.72 mg/kg intravenous, 20 mg/kg intramuscular, and 18.5 mg/kg subcutaneous) of *C. atrox* are far less toxic than many other rattlesnakes. Nonetheless, because adults have long fangs and large venom glands, they can deliver a substantial amount of venom in a single bite.

Because it is large, has strongly defensive behavior, is abundant, and has a wide geographic distribution, more people in North America sustain bites from *C. atrox* than any other species of rattlesnake. With large individuals, severe envenomation is not rare and lethal bites occur annually.

Similar looking species

The species most commonly confused with *C. atrox* is the Mojave Rattlesnake, *Crotalus scutulatus* (see pages 112–118). Newborns of these species are particularly difficult to distinguish.

The species most commonly confused with *C. atrox* (a) is the Mojave Rattlesnake, *Crotalus scutulatus* (b). Newborns of these species are particularly difficult to distinguish. Photos by W. Wells.

DISTRIBUTION & HABITATS

Miller and colleagues (Miller et al., 1982) did not report *Crotalus atrox* from GRCA or its immediate vicinity. Its presence in the Grand Canyon, though limited, has recently been confirmed (see below).

Schuett and colleagues (Schuett et al., 2016a, p. 346) wrote about the occurrence of *Crotalus atrox* at or near the Grand Canyon:

More recent records have verified sightings of *C. atrox* on the edges of its range in the Grand Canyon and Lake Mead. The first verified record of *C. atrox* in the Grand Canyon is in Mohave County in 1997, near the confluence of Diamond Creek and the Colorado River (35° 46'N, 113° 22' W; Brown, 2000). Brown (2003) also found the first verified record of *C. atrox* in the upper Lake Mead region and furthest downstream record for the Grand Canyon region, at Lake Mead National Recreation Area, Pierce Ferry (36° 07' N, 114° 00' W) and another *C. atrox* near Diamond Creek, Mohave County. Between the aforementioned localities, *C. atrox* has been documented away from the Colorado River in the Grand Wash Cliffs at an elevation of 4600 ft (1400 m) (M. Feldner, unpubl. data; UAZ 57518-PSV). Questionable localities include a SDNHM (San Diego Natural History Museum) specimen georeferenced from Grand View of the Grand Canyon, Coconino County, Arizona. This is not from Coconino County but a different Grand View, in a different county (Spencer, 2003).

ECOLOGY & BEHAVIOR

Over the past 20 years, radio-telemetric studies of *C. atrox* have been conducted in various locations in Arizona (reviewed by Schuett et al., 2016a, b; Taylor and Booth, 2016). Similar work has not been published on this taxon elsewhere in its extensive range, and no studies have been conducted at Grand Canyon National Park.

A long-term (15-years) field study on a population of *C. atrox* (Suizo Mountains, Pinal Co. Arizona) by Schuett and colleagues (Schuett et al., 2016a, b and references therein) has provided in-depth information on social and parental behavior, annual movements, diet, winter den behavior, kin genetics, paternity, and sexual selection.

POPULATION STATUS & CONSERVATION

Most populations of *C. atrox* do not seem to be under direct threat of extirpation. Currently, in most regions of Arizona, *C. atrox* can be legally collected or harvested with a non-game hunting license.

Male-male combat in *Crotalus atrox* near Tucson Mountains, Arizona. Photo by T. J. Allen.

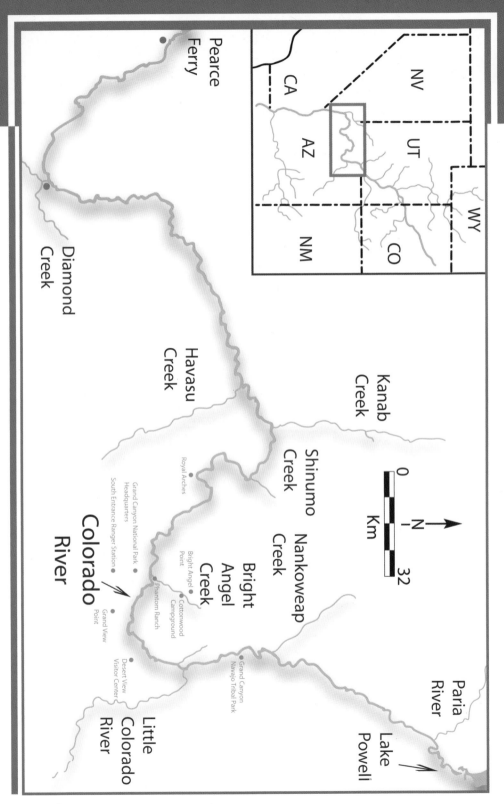

Map 5 (opposite page)

Distribution of the Western Diamond-backed Rattlesnake (*Crotalus atrox*) within and near Grand Canyon National Park. The red dots signify known sites, but are not exhaustive. For more information on *C. atrox*, see Schuett et al. (2016a, b).

Black-tailed Rattlesnake

Crotalus molossus

COMMON NAMES

In Arizona (including the Grand Canyon) the most common accepted name for this species is Black-tailed Rattlesnake. It also has been called the Northern Black-tailed Rattlesnake (Klauber, 1972). A recent study of eastern populations in New Mexico, Texas, and northern Mexico formerly known as *C. m. molossus* revealed a new species (*Crotalus ornatus*); its common name is Ornate Rattlesnake (Anderson & Greenbaum, 2012).

SCIENTIFIC NAMES

The scientific name for the Black-tailed Rattlesnake (*Crotalus molossus*) has undergone little change since it was first described in 1853 by Baird and Girard (1853; but see Persons et al., 2016). The original description of *Crotalus molossus* is based on a specimen from Grant County, New Mexico (museum type specimen is at the United States National Museum number 485). For more details, see Laurence Klauber (1972; recent reviewed by Persons and colleagues, 2016).

Recently, Trevor Persons and colleagues (Persons et al., 2016) state (p. 457):

The specific epithet *molossus* is Latin, derived from the Greek Molossos, referring to the district in ancient Epirus famous for its mastiff-like hounds…the name may be an allusion to the species' blunt (mastiff-like) muzzle.

DESCRIPTION
Body size
Older adults of the Black-tailed Rattlesnake can be large-sized (length and girth), and they sometimes attain a total length exceeding 1200 mm, or over 4 feet. In the Chiricahua Mountains of southeastern Arizona, a large individual was reported by investigators David Hardy and Harry Greene (1995); it was 1241 mm (snout-vent length, SVL) and its body mass was 1011 g. Most adults are smaller in length (< 1000 mm SVL) and body mass is less (range: 500-800 g) (Roger Repp, Gordon Schuett, Martin Feldner, unpublished data).

Sexual size dimorphism (SSD) is a common phenomenon in rattlesnakes. Males typically attain greater sizes (length and mass) than females, which is the situation in the Black-tailed Rattlesnake (Klauber, 1972; David Hardy, personal communication). Like so many other species of rattlesnakes, there is variation in adult size (Klauber, 1972; see Amarello et al., 2009).

The smallest reproductive female (presence of enlarged follicles or ova) measured 653 mm snout-vent length. Neonates measure 272 mm SVL (229–315 mm, n = 22) and have a body mass of 11–28 g. Neonates from the Suizo Mountains ranged from 301–315 mm SVL, and were 21–27 g (Roger Repp and Martin Feldner, unpublished data).

Pattern & coloration
Newborn and juveniles of the Black-tailed Rattlesnake often bear a strong resemblance to the adults, with fairly prominent hues of yellow, yellow-green tans, whites, and blacks; however, their coloration is overall more subdued. In populations from xeric (desert) areas of Arizona (e.g., Suizo Mountains, Tinajas Altas Mountains), both young and adults are subtly pale and quite distinct

when compared to populations of the Sky Islands and to those found further north, such as in the Grand Canyon. These individuals from xeric regions are commonly various shades of gray with paler crossbands (see review by Persons et al., 2016).

A newborn Black-tailed Rattlesnake from the Chiricahua Mountains, Cochise County, Arizona. Photo by C. Smith.

With maturity at about 4-years-old, the ground color of some individuals from several populations undergoes a dramatic change to brilliant yellow and yellow-orange hues, with bold, dark cross bands that have irregular edges; these bands are sometimes bordered in white. The front region of the head is darkly marked; the dark color extends to the eye and continues as dark post-ocular stripes. True to its common moniker, the tail is often solid black or very dark.

An adult Black-tailed Rattlesnake from the Tinajas Altas Mountains, Arizona. Photo by W. Wells

A possible *C. molossus* x *C. ornatus* hybrid from New Mexico. Photo by A. Bentley.

Venom

The venom of the Black-tailed Rattlesnake has not been studied to the extent of other species, like the Mojave Rattlesnake, Prairie Rattlesnake, and members of the Western Group.

Stephen Mackessy (2008) reported that Black-tailed Rattlesnakes have a Type I venom, which is characterized by high metalloproteinase activity and moderate lethal toxicity. However, owing to their large head, large venom glands, and long fangs, large individuals are capable of delivering serious bites to humans.

Human envenomation by the Black-tailed Rattlesnake (*Crotalus molossus*) is relatively rare, owing to their calm disposition and general preference for more rugged terrain distant from human activity. David Hardy and colleagues (Hardy et al., 1982) reported two cases of human envenomation by *Crotalus molossus* in Arizona in which local venom effects were significant, but the individuals recovered without permanent tissue damage. David Hardy and Kelly Zamudio (Hardy & Zamudio, 2006) discussed a severe case of human envenomation by *Crotalus molossus* in southeastern Arizona that resulted in compartment syndrome in which full recovery took almost two years.

Clearly, more field and laboratory work will be required before we have a definitive understanding of venom variability in the Black-tailed Rattlesnake.

Similar looking species

The Black-tailed Rattlesnake is so distinctive at all of its life stages that it is unlikely to be confused with any other species of rattlesnake in the Grand Canyon or in nearby areas.

DISTRIBUTION & HABITATS

The Black-tailed Rattlesnake (*Crotalus molossus*) has an extensive distribution in the United States (Arizona, western New Mexico) and Mexico (reviewed by Campbell & Lamar, 2004); in Arizona it is the most widely distributed rattlesnake species (Brennan & Holycross, 2006; Persons et al., 2016). In areas of south-central New Mexico and Texas, the Black-tailed Rattlesnake is replaced by the Ornate Rattlesnake (*Crotalus ornatus*), which looks similar to *Crotalus molossus*, but the ground color tends to be largely shades of gray rather than the tans, yellows, and browns; also the cross bands (blotches) are considerably paler than in *C. molossus*.

A neonate *Crotalus ornatus* from West Texas. Photo by N. Fields.

Recently, Trevor B. Persons and colleagues (Persons et al., 2016) reviewed the ecology of *Crotalus molossus*. They state (p. 46) the following with respect to its distribution in Arizona:

> It occurs along and below the Mogollon Rim, and it ranges as far northwest as the Hualapai Mountains and the western Grand Canyon…although infrequently found within Grand Canyon itself, *C. molossus* has been documented along both the north and south rims as far east as Tuckup and Havasu Canyons, respectively … and as far west as the north

end of the Grand Wash Cliffs south of the Colorado River (Martin Feldner and John Slone, unpublished data). The species is likely fairly common in this region, but is rarely observed due to the inaccessible terrain occupied. While the distribution is fairly continuous in the rugged, upland habitats common along the Mogollon Rim and throughout much of the Madrean Sky Island region of southeastern Arizona, as well as in the Arizona Upland subdivision of the Sonoran Desert, its occurrence in the southwestern part of the state is generally restricted to isolated arid mountain ranges that dot the predominantly low-lying Lower Colorado River subdivision. Within this desert area, however, *C. molossus* is surprisingly widespread … and has been documented from most of the major ranges in the region, as far west as the Gila Mountains east of Yuma.

Of the 16 species of rattlesnakes that occur in Arizona, the Black-tailed Rattlesnake clearly inhabits the most wide ranging habitats, from low elevation, creosote-dominated desertscrub through coniferous forests on mountains; it is found in all major biotic communities (Brennan & Holycross, 2006; reviewed by Persons et al., 2016). More specifically, Sonoran desertscrub, Mohave desertscrub, Great Basin desertscrub, semi-desert grassland, interior chaparral, pinyon-juniper woodland, and various broadleaf riparian, and xeric-riparian vegetation types (Persons et al., 2016).

ECOLOGY & BEHAVIOR

There are short-term ecological studies conducted on the Black-tailed Rattlesnake, including Daniel Beck's work in the Tucson Mountains, Arizona. Long-term studies are rare. In one case, using radio-telemetry, one team (Roger Repp, Gordon Schuett, and Martin Feldner) has studied the Black-tailed Rattlesnake in the Suizo Mountains (Pinal County, Arizona) from 2001 to 2016. Recently, Persons and colleagues (Persons et al., 2016, p. 467) summarized aspects of the Suizo research:

> [*Crotalus*] *molossus* commonly emerge from overwintering sites by early March, followed by a 'staging' period where snakes bask and move little for several weeks before beginning a period of hunting rocky sites, often associated with woodrat middens. By the end of April most snakes have begun to use bajada and wash edge habitats in their active season ranges where they remain through late September to early November when they again return to rocky hillsides and hunt until returning to upland overwintering sites. Activity in the Suizos is diurnal early and late in the year, with nocturnal activity beginning by early May and lasting through early November, though snakes will remain on the surface for hours after sunrise even during the hottest times of the year.

At this point in time, there are no published ecological studies of the Black-tailed Rattlesnake in the Grand Canyon.

POPULATION STATUS & CONSERVATION

Because it occurs in the Grand Canyon National Park and nearby areas that are protected (e.g., Indian Nation Lands, National Forests), the Black-tailed Rattlesnake populations are safe from development and large-scale human persecution in northern Arizona. However, populations close to human activity in Phoenix and Tucson in central Arizona are less safe and have been adversely affected both directly and indirectly (see Herrmann, 2016).

Elsewhere in its extensive range in Arizona, the greatest immediate threat to this species is climate change. Recent modeling work on other species of rattlesnakes (e.g., *Crotalus cerberus*) that occupy the Colorado Plateau has shown that this region is extremely vulnerable to climate change and wildfires (Douglas et al., 2016). Other regions of the Southwest are vulnerable to similar kinds of ecological impacts. Most rattlesnake populations are adversely affected by human expansion, with the accompanying degradation of habitat, including new highways and agricultural expansion.

In Arizona, a valid state hunting license is required to collect all species of reptiles, except for protected species. Arizona Game and Fish Commission Order 43 stipulates a bag limit for *Crotalus molossus* of four animals per year or in possession live or dead; they may be taken or killed at any time of year. Commercial collecting of native reptiles and amphibians is prohibited in Arizona.

Newborn (several days old) and pre-shed (note blue eyes) Black-tailed Rattlesnakes inspecting their world away from their mother. Suizo Mountains, Pinal County, Arizona. Photo by M. Feldner.

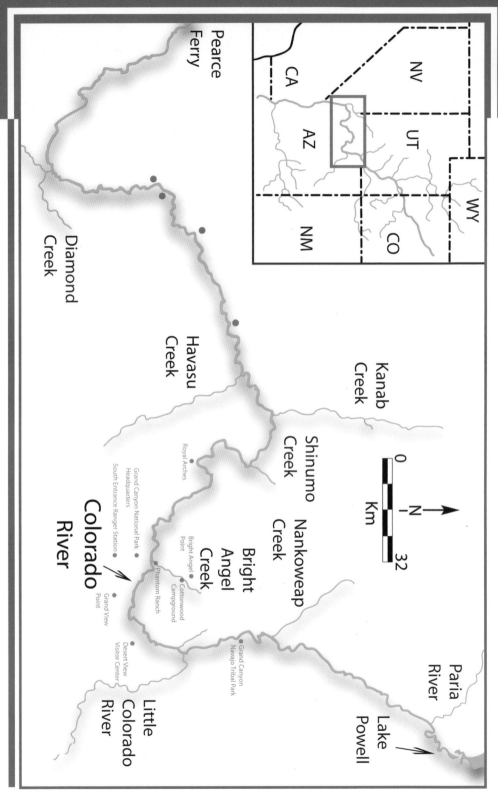

Map 6 (opposite page)

Distribution of the Black-tailed Rattlesnake (*Crotalus molossus*) within the GRCA. The red dots signify known sites, but are not exhaustive. For more information on *C. molossus* see Persons et al. (2016).

Southwestern Speckled Rattlesnake

Crotalus pyrrhus

COMMON NAMES

The most widely accepted common name for this species is the Southwestern Speckled Rattlesnake. Other names include White Rattlesnake, Bleached Rattlesnake, and Mitchell's Rattlesnake. In western Arizona, ranchers sometimes refer to this species as the Red Mojave Rattlesnake, as described by the specific epithet *pyrrhus* (Latin for "flame-colored").

Populations of the Southwestern Speckled Rattlesnakes from central Arizona are often pink-orange in ground color. Further north, in the Grand Canyon and nearby areas, adults of the Southwestern Speckled Rattlesnake are often pink, peach, salmon, or vermilion in coloration, and speckles in other colors such as white, gray and black. Thus, it is commonly misidentified as the Grand Canyon Rattlesnake (*Crotalus abyssus*).

SCIENTIFIC NAMES

The Southwestern Speckled Rattlesnake was originally described by the American explorer Edward Drinker Cope in 1866. Seven decades later, the self-taught

An adult Southwestern Speckled Rattlesnake from the western area of GRCA. Note the pale pink coloration resembling *C. abyssus*. Photo by B. O'Connor.

snake expert Laurence Klauber re-named this rattlesnake as a subspecies of *Crotalus mitchellii* (*C. m. pyrrhus*) (Klauber, 1936).

Over the years with increasing study and analysis the scientific name has changed again; 60 years after Klauber's work the Southwestern Speckled Rattlesnake has been given full species status and a new name, *Crotalus pyrrhus* (Meik, 2016). The Speckled Rattlesnake Group has recently been reviewed by Jesse Meik (Meik, 2016).

DESCRIPTION
Body size
Adults of the Southwestern Speckled Rattlesnake can be medium- to large sized, and sometimes attain a maximum total length of nearly 1000 mm, or about 3 feet (Meik, 2016).

Like many other species, the Southwestern Speckled Rattlesnake shows geographic variation in body size. Some of the largest Southwestern Speckled Rattlesnakes are found in chaparral habitats in California, where large males can exceed 1200 mm (48 inches), or 4 feet, in total length, and 1 kg (2.2 lbs.) in body mass (Klauber, 1936, 1972).

In general, the Southwestern Speckled Rattlesnake is relatively small in most of western Arizona and northeastern Baja California, Mexico (Meik 2016). Speckled Rattlesnakes from the Tinajas Altas Mountains, (Yuma County, Arizona) are small and quite pale (white). Eight adult males from the Tinajas Altas Mountains had a average (mean) snout-vent length of 543 mm (21.4 inches) and a mean mass of 132 g. From the same population, 5 adult females had a mean snout-vent length of 446 mm (17.6 inches) and a mean mass of 74 g (unpublished data of Martin Feldner, as reported by Meik, 2016, p. 526).

Sexual size dimorphism (SSD) is a common phenomenon in rattlesnakes, typically with males attaining greater sizes than females, which is the situation in the Southwestern Speckled Rattlesnake.

Overall, neonates average 259 mm (10.2 inches) in total length and 22.4 g in mass. The smallest reproductive female was 552 mm (21.7 inches) in snout-vent length; reproductive males are similar in size (512 mm snout-vent length).

Pattern and coloration

Typical of most other rattlesnakes, neonates and juveniles tend to be less vibrant in coloration than adults. As mentioned earlier, the coloration of adults is dependent to a large degree on geographic location. No other species of rattlesnake is more variable in coloration than the Speckled Rattlesnake. With maturity at about 3-4 years, they can range in body color from tan, beige, straw, gray, (blue-gray) and white to bright pink, orange, and vermillion. The common name (Speckled Rattlesnake) refers to the speckling pattern on the ground color, making the Speckled Rattlesnake one of the most beautiful species.

Newborn Southwestern Speckled Rattlesnake from Maricopa County, Arizona. Photo by M. Feldner.

A Southwestern Speckled Rattlesnake from Tinajas Altas Mountains, Yuma County, Arizona. Photo by W. Wells.

Venom

Little work has been done to characterize the venom of the Southwestern Speckled Rattlesnake and its closest relatives. Venom characteristics of the Baja Speckled Rattlesnake (*Crotalus m. mitchellii*) differ considerably from the Southwestern Speckled Rattlesnake (*Crotalus pyrrhus*), with the former being much more toxic in mice (LD$_{50}$ 0.13 – 0.24 mg/kg) but tends to have a lower yield of venom (Klauber, 1936). Interestingly, the venom of *Crotalus m. mitchellii* lacks hemorrhagic activity and has a Mojave-like toxin similar to the Mojave Rattlesnake (*Crotalus scutulatus*). Recently, Stephen Mackessy's laboratory (Mackessy, 2008) has shown that venom of the Southwestern Speckled Rattlesnake is of moderate lethal toxicity and is characterized by high metalloproteinase (enzyme) activity. Similar to the Western Group, high lethal toxicity in rattlesnake venoms is incongruent with low metalloproteinase activity.

Clearly, more field and laboratory work will be required before we have a definitive understanding of venom variability in the Speckled Rattlesnake Group.

Similar looking species

The Southwestern Speckled Rattlesnake is distinctive at all of its life stages; it is not likely to be confused with any other species of rattlesnake except the Tiger Rattlesnake (*Crotalus tigris*) (next page top image). In the Grand Canyon and nearby areas, identification may be confused with pale (orange or pink) individuals of the Grand Canyon Rattlesnake (*Crotalus abyssus*) (next page bottom image).

An adult Tiger Rattlesnake (*Crotalus tigris*) from Arizona. Photo by B. O'Connor.

An adult Grand Canyon Rattlesnake (*Crotalus abyssus*) from Arizona. Photo by B. O'Connor.

An adult Southwestern Speckled Rattlesnake from the western area of GRCA. Photo by B. O'Connor.

DISTRIBUTION & HABITATS

In Meik's (Meik, 2016, pp. 531-62) recent review of the Southwestern Speckled Rattlesnake (*Crotalus pyrrhus*), he describes its expansive geographic range as follows:

> *Crotalus pyrrhus* is endemic to the Mohave-Sonoran Desert system from extreme southwestern Utah and southern Nevada, through southeastern California, western Arizona, northwestern Sonora, Mexico, and throughout Baja California, Mexico, north of the Vizcaíno region. Populations also occur on various islands in the Gulf of California, including El Muerto, Smith, Piojo, and Cabeza de Caballo islands.

In Arizona, the Speckled Rattlesnake is found in the Mohave Desertscrub, Lower Colorado River, and Arizona Upland subdivisions of the Desertscrub Formation. From the Virgin River Gorge in extreme northwestern Arizona, its distribution extends southward along the Virgin Mountains and follows the Colorado River east into the Grand Canyon. Within the Grand Cayon, it occurs as far as the mouth of Havasu Canyon; southward it can be found throughout Peach Springs Canyon.

ECOLOGY & BEHAVIOR

Several ecological studies have been conducted on the Southwestern Speckled Rattlesnake, but none in the Grand Canyon.

Xavier Glaudas and his colleague Javier Rodríguez-Robles (Glaudas & Rodríguez-Robles, 2011a) tracked adult Southwestern Speckled Rattlesnakes implanted with radio-transmitters in the area of the Eldorado Mountains (Clark County, Nevada) in the eastern part of the Mojave Desert. At this site, mating occurs in spring (late April to early June) after emergence from overwintering dens. Males and females traveled further per unit time in the mating season compared to the post-mating season, and males made longer distances movements per unit time than females. Importantly, males with larger home ranges during the mating season had a greater number of potential mating partners. Males fight for access to females, and males of larger size are more likely to acquire females (see page 108). This work has supplied important and hard-to-obtain information on the mating systems of rattlesnakes (see Clark et al., 2014).

In another study of the same population, Glaudas and Rodríguez-Robles (Glaudas & Rodríguez-Robles, 2011b) investigated the diet. Importantly, they found that at the macrohabitat level, selection and avoidance of particular macrohabitats by the Southwestern Speckled Rattlesnakes were positively correlated with rodent abundance during the post-mating season. Furthermore, because most snake foraging activity occurs during the post-mating season, these authors state that this finding suggests that the Southwestern Speckled Rattlesnake selects macrohabitats that increase prey encounter rates. However, in contrast, rodent abundance was relatively low at the microhabitats that were selected by the snakes. Consequently, higher prey abundance in the preferred macrohabitat did not translate into increased access to prey at the snake micro-habitats, indicating that prey distribution may not be a constant predictor of predator habitat choice across spatial scales. Their study emphasizes the challenges that ambush predators face when hunting prey that is risk-sensitive.

POPULATION STATUS & CONSERVATION

The Southwestern Speckled Rattlesnake (*Crotalus pyrrhus*) remains common in suitable areas and habitats, and it may reach high densities under ideal conditions even in metropolitan areas such as isolated mountain parks in Phoenix, Arizona (Meik, 2016). By virtue of its presence in the Grand Canyon National Park, the Southwestern Speckled Rattlesnake gains protection from development and large-scale human persecution in Arizona. Research on populations in the GRCA is only by permission, and time-sensitive scientific permits are issued only to qualified individuals.

Like other rattlesnakes and other species of flora and fauna, perhaps the greatest immediate threat to the Southwestern Speckled Rattlesnake is climate change. Recent modeling work on other species of rattlesnakes (e.g., *Crotalus cerberus*) of the Colorado Plateau has shown that this region is extremely vulnerable to climate change and wildfires (Douglas et al., 2016). Other regions of the United States, particularly the Southwest, are vulnerable to similar kinds of impacts, but also human expansion with accompanying degradation of habitat.

In Arizona, a valid state hunting license is required to collect all species of reptiles, except for protected species. Arizona Game and Fish Commission Order 43 stipulates a bag limit for *Crotalus pyrrhus* of four animals per year or in possession live or dead; they may be taken or killed at any time of year. Commercial collecting of native reptiles and amphibians is prohibited in Arizona.

Two adult male Southwestern Speckled Rattlesnakes engaged in combat. Maricopa County, Arizona. Photo by B. O'Connor.

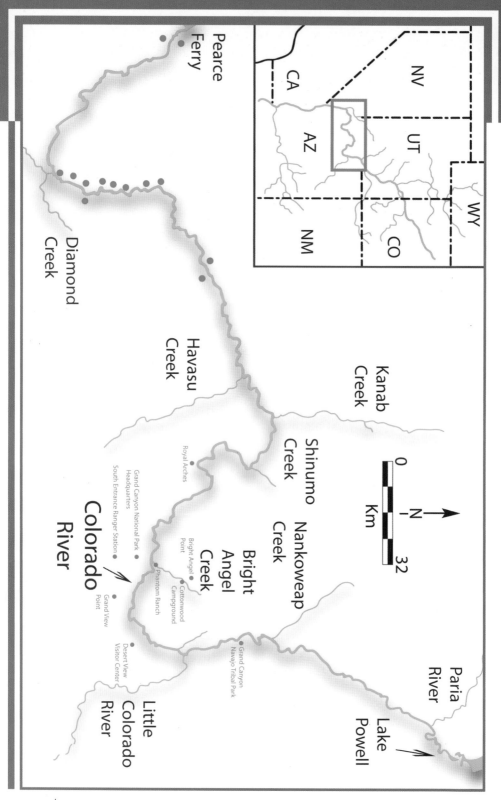

Map7 (opposite page)

Distribution of the Southwestern Speckled Rattlesnake (*Crotalus pyrrhus*) within the GRCA. The red dots denote known sites, but are not exhaustive. For more information on *C. pyrrhus* see Douglas et al. (2006, 2007) and Meik (2016).

Mojave Rattlesnake

Crotalus scutulatus

COMMON NAMES

The most widely accepted common name for this species is the Mojave Rattlesnake. Other common names are Green Rattlesnake and Mojave Green Rattlesnake. The spelling of the word "Mojave" or "Mohave" has been a subject of debate. Charles Lowe (1986), Campbell and Lamar (2004), and Cardwell (2016) prefer the use of "Mohave." Lawrence Jones (2016) discussed that the spelling should be with "j" but the SSAR committee voted to continue to use "h" for the vernacular (SSAR. 2017, pp.64-65). Here, owing to stability, we follow the suggestions by Jones (2016). Spanish names include vibora de cascabel and vibora serrana (Campbell and Lamar, 2004).

SCIENTIFIC NAMES

In 1861 Kennicott named the taxon *Caudisona scutulata*, but he did not elaborate on his rationale for choosing the specific name. Researcher Michael Cardwell (Cardwell, 2016), feels that Kennicott named the animal *scutulata* in recognition of the large crown scales (scutes) on the head, which are characteristic of the species. Later, it was renamed *Crotalus scutulatus* (see Klauber 1972).

DESCRIPTION

Body size

Crotalus scutulatus is a medium-sized rattlesnake (Klauber, 1972). Individuals over 1000 mm in total length (excluding the rattle) are uncommon. A record-size male *C. scutulatus* from Arizona (Pinal County) measured 1144 mm SVL and 1236 total length (Mrinalini et al., 2015)

Pattern & coloration

The dorsum is typically prominently marked with dark blotches that are diamond-shaped and bordered by darker scales, which are, in turn, surrounded by a row of light-colored scales. The blotches transition into transverse body bands on the caudal portion of the body. The dorsal blotches or rhombs barely reach the midline of the sides, especially anteriorly, but they are sometimes separated by one or two scale rows of background color. Lateral spots of the same color as the center of the dorsal rhombs, although smaller and less distinct than the dorsal markings, are usually present on the first few scale rows on each side. The background coloration is olive-green or greenish-gray, but infrequently can be brown, yellowish-brown, or rarely nearly all-yellow. The venter is generally green or yellow and unmarked (Cardwell, 2016).

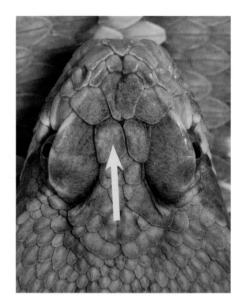

Over the years since its description, the meaning of the species name for *Crotalus scutulatus* has been debated by authorities, but it likely refers to the large intersupraocular scales on the dorsum of the head (arrow). Photo by M. D. Cardwell.

A consistent pattern of *C. scutulatus* is the angle of the light-colored post-ocular stripe (just behind the eye) on the lateral side of the head. In *C. scutulatus*, and also in the Prairie Rattlesnake (*C. viridis*), this stripe angles posteriorly and passes above the corner of the mouth.

The tail tends to be distinct from the body pattern and coloration, often with black and white (grey) bands. Unlike *C. atrox*, the tail is sometimes not distinct from the body pattern and coloration.

Venom

The Mojave Rattlesnake should be treated as dangerously venomous. Except for an area in central Arizona, the venom of *C. scutulatus* venom contains a powerful neurotoxin (Mojave toxin), which is responsible for the low LD_{50} values in mice. Individuals having Mojave toxin are described as having venom-A, and those lacking the Mojave toxin as having venom-B (reviewed by Cardwell, 2016).

Mojave Rattlesnake (*Crotalus scutulatus*). Aubrey Valley, Coconino County, Arizona. Photo by W. Wells.

Bites and envenomation that involve individuals with venom-A are generally more serious and produce symptoms that often include lethargy, hypotension, drooping eyelids, and difficulty speaking and swallowing; diaphragm function and respiration may be compromised in some cases (Cardwell, 2016).

Similar looking species
The Mojave Rattlesnake, especially as newborns, most closely resembles the Western Diamond-backed Rattlesnake (*C. atrox*).

DISTRIBUTION & HABITATS
Similar to the situation with the Western Diamond-backed Rattlesnake (*C. atrox*), the Mojave Rattlesnake seems to have a limited and spotty distribution in the Grand Canyon and its immediate environs. As stated by Miller and colleagues (Miller et al., 1982, p. 132):

> Its natural range extends to extreme northwest Arizona; and it seems probable that this species could enter the Canyon from the southwest regions. Unconfirmed reports have this species occurring in Havasu Canyon.

Recently, Cardwell (2016, p. 573) wrote about the occurrence of *C. scutulatus* at or near the Grand Canyon:

> I know of only two museum specimens verified as *C. scutulatus* that are accompanied by detailed location data in Coconino County – but just

barely. USNM (United States National Museum) 218683 was reported to have been collected in July 1977 crossing United States Hwy 66 at Hyde Park Road, which is about 8 km east of the Mohave-Coconino County line. UAZ (University of Arizona) 52116 was photographed in May 2000 on Forestry Road 492, just east of Drake and about 800 m east of the Yavapai-Coconino County line in the Kaibab National Forest. Thus it appears that *C. scutulatus* only occurs in Coconino County along the southwestern margin where suitable grassland habitat intrudes from lower elevations. A few old museum specimens are recorded from much farther northeast in Coconino County but their locality data are vague and the lack of subsequent specimens from the area renders their validity highly questionable. In Mohave County, *C. scutulatus* is found throughout the county's Mohave Desert Scrub habitat, including near the mouth of the Grand Canyon and the vicinity of the Virgin River, as well as in the Semi-Desert Grassland of the Hualapai Valley. Disjunct areas of Great Basin Grassland habitat in the areas of the Hualapai Indian Reservation and Peach Springs have also produced museum specimens of *C. scutulatus*.

ECOLOGY & BEHAVIOR
There are few studies available on the ecology and behavior of *C. scutulatus* in Arizona (for a review, see Cardwell, 2016; but see Schuett et al., 2002; Zancolli et al., 2016). No ecological study has been done on populations of *C. scutulatus* in or near the Grand Canyon.

POPULATION STATUS & CONSERVATION
Most populations of *C. scutulatus* in Arizona do not seem to be under direct threat of extirpation. Currently, in most regions, *C. scutulatus* can be legally collected or harvested in Arizona with a non-game hunting license.

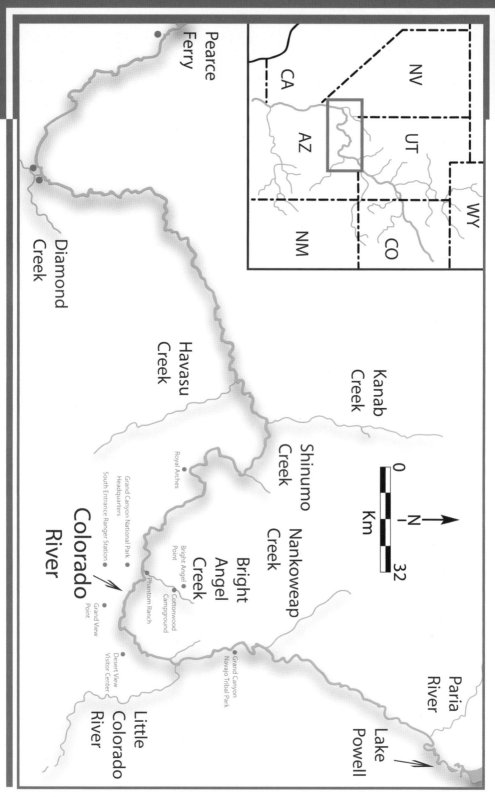

Map 8 (opposite page)

Distribution of the Mojave Rattlesnake (*Crotalus scutulatus*) within and near Grand Canyon National Park. The red dots signify known sites, but are not exhaustive. For more information on *C. scutulatus*, see Cardwell (2016).

Literature Cited and References

General

Grant, P. R., and B. R. Grant (1992). Hybridization in bird species. Science 256: 193–197.

Mead, J. I., and T. R. Van Devender (1981). Late Holocene diet of *Bassariscus astutus* in the Grand Canyon, Arizona. Journal of Mammalogy 62: 439–442.

Wagner, G. P. (2015). Evolutionary innovations and novelties: Let us get down to business! Zoologischer Anzeiger-A Journal of Comparative Zoology 256: 75–81.

Wagner, G. P. (2016). What is "homology thinking" and what is it for? Journal of Experimental Zoology (Molecular Development & Evolution) 326B: 3–8.

Reptiles

Brennan, T. C, and A. T. Holycross (2006). *Amphibians and Reptiles in Arizona.* Arizona Game & Fish Department, Phoenix, Arizona.

Campbell, J. A., and W. W. Lamar (2004). *The Venomous Reptiles of the Western Hemisphere,* 2 vols. Comstock Publishing Associates, Cornell University Press, Ithaca, New York.

Durham, F. E. (1956). Amphibians and reptiles of the North Rim, Grand Canyon, Arizona. Herpetologica 12: 220–224.

Ernst, C. H., and E. M Ernst (2012). *Venomous Reptiles of the United States, Canada, and Northern Mexico,* 2 vols. The Johns Hopkins University Press, Baltimore, Maryland.

Miller, D. M., R. A. Young, T. W. Gatlin, and J. A. Richardson (1982). *Amphibians and Reptiles of the Grand Canyon.* Grand Canyon Natural History Association, Monograph No. 4. Classic Printers, Prescott, Arizona.

Stebbins, R. C. (2003). *A Field Guide to Western Reptiles & Amphibians, 3rd edn.* Houghton Mifflin, Boston, Massachusetts.

Snakes

Baird, S. F., and C. Girard (1853). *Catalogue of North American Reptiles in the Museum of the Smithsonian Institution. Part I-Serpents.* Government Printing Office, Washington, DC.

Duvall, D., S. J. Arnold, and G. W. Schuett (1992). Pitviper mating systems: Ecological potential, sexual selection, and microevolution. Pp. 321–336 *In* J. A. Campbell, and E. D. Brodie Jr. (Eds.), *Biology of the Pitvipers*. Selva, Tyler, Texas.

Fowlie, J. A. (1965). *The Snakes of Arizona*. Azul Quinta Press, Fallbrook, California.

Greene, H. W. (1997). *Snakes. The Evolution of Mystery*. University of California Press, Berkeley, California.

Greene, H. W., P. G. May, D. L. Hardy, J. L. Sciturro, and T. M. Farrell. (2002). Parental behavior by vipers. Pp.179–206 *In* G. W. Schuett, M. Höggren, M. E. Douglas, and H. W. Greene (Eds.), *Biology of the Vipers*. Eagle Mountain Publishing LC, Eagle Mountain, Utah.

Schuett, G. W., M. Höggren, M. E. Douglas, and H. W. Greene (Eds.) (2002). *Biology of the Vipers*. Eagle Mountain Publishing, LC, Eagle Mountain, Utah.

Rattlesnakes

Amarello, M., E. M. Nowak, E. N. Taylor, G. W. Schuett, R. A. Repp, P. C. Rosen, and D. L. Hardy (2010). Potential environmental influences on variation in body size and sexual size dimorphism among Arizona populations of the Western Diamond-backed Rattlesnake (*Crotalus atrox*). Journal of Arid Environments 74: 1,443–1,449.

Anderson, C. G., and E. Greenbaum (2012). Phylogeography of northern populations of the Black-tailed Rattlesnake (*Crotalus molossus* Baird and Girard, 1853), with the revalidation of *C. ornatus* Hallowell, 1854. Herpetological Monographs 26: 19–57.

Ashton, K. G. (2003). Movements and mating behavior of adult male Midget Faded Rattlesnakes, *Crotalus oreganus concolor*, in Wyoming. Copeia 2003: 190–194.

Ashton, K. G., and T. M. Patton (2001). Movement and reproductive biology of female Midget Faded Rattlesnakes, *Crotalus viridis concolor*, in Wyoming. Copeia 2001: 229–234.

Bauder, J. M., H. Akenson, and C. R. Peterson (2015). Movement patterns of Prairie Rattlesnakes (*Crotalus v. viridis*) across a mountainous landscape in a designated wilderness area. Journal of Herpetology 49: 377–387.

Brown, N. L. (2000). Geographic Distribution. *Crotalus atrox* (Western Diamond-backed Rattlesnake). Herpetological Review 31: 54–55.

Campbell, J. A., and W. W. Lamar (2004). Venomous Reptiles of the Western Hemisphere, 2 vols. Cornell University Press, Ithaca, New York.

Cardwell, M. D. (2016). Species Accounts. *Crotalus scutulatus* (Mohave Rattlesnake). Pp. 563–605. *In* G. W. Schuett, M. J. Feldner, C. F. Smith, and R. S. Reiserer (Eds.), *Rattlesnakes of Arizona, vol. 1*. ECO Publishing, Rodeo, New Mexico.

Clark, R. W., G. W. Schuett, R. A. Repp, M. Amarello, C. F. Smith, and H.-W. Herrmann (2014). Mating systems, reproductive success, and sexual selection in a secretive species: A case study of the Western Diamond-backed Rattlesnake, *Crotalus atrox*. PLoS ONE 9: e90616.

Da Silva, S. L., J. R. Almeida, L. M. Resende, W. Martins et al. (2011). Isolation and characterization of a natriuretic peptide from *Crotalus oreganus abyssus* (Grand Canyon Rattlesnake) and its effects on systemic blood pressure and nitrite levels. International Journal of Peptide Research and Therapeutics 17: 165–173.

Da Silva, S. L., C. A. Dias-Junior, P. A. Baldasso, D. C. S. Damico et al (2012). Vascular effects and electrolyte homeostasis of the natriuretic peptide isolated from *Crotalus oreganus abyssus* (North American Grand Canyon Rattlesnake) venom. Peptides 36: 206–212.

Davis, M. A. (2012). Morphometrics, Molecular Ecology and Multivariate Environmental Niche Define the Evolutionary History of the Western Rattlesnake (*Crotalus viridis*) Complex. Unpublished dissertation. University of Illinois Urbana Champaign, Champaign, Illinois.

Davis, M. A., M. R. Douglas, C. T. Webb, M. L. Collyer, A. T. Holycross, C. W. Painter, L. K. Kamees, and M. E. Douglas (2015). Nowhere to go but up: Impacts of climate change on demography of a short-range endemic (*Crotalus willardi obscurus*) in the sky islands of southwestern North America. PLoS ONE 10: e0131067.

Davis, M. A. (2016). The western rattlesnake complex: 200 years of intrigue and change. Pp. 39–43 *In* G. W. Schuett, M. J. Feldner, C. F. Smith, and R. S. Reiserer (Eds.), *Rattlesnakes of Arizona, vol. 1*. ECO Publishing, Rodeo, New Mexico.

Davis, M. A., and M. E. Douglas (2016). Species Accounts. *Crotalus viridis* (Prairie Rattlesnake). Pp. 289–332 *In* G. W. Schuett, M. J. Feldner, C. F. Smith, and R. S. Reiserer (Eds.), *Rattlesnakes of Arizona, vol. 1*. ECO Publishing, Rodeo, New Mexico.

Davis, M. A, M. R. Douglas, M. L. Collyer, and M. E. Douglas (2016a). Deconstructing a species-complex: Geometric morphometric and molecular analyses define species in the Western Rattlesnake (*Crotalus viridis*). PLOS ONE 11(2): e0149712.

Davis, M. A, M. J. Feldner, and G. W. Schuett (2016b). Species Accounts. *Crotalus cerberus* (Arizona Black Rattlesnake). Pp. 109–177 *In* G. W. Schuett, M. J. Feldner, C. F. Smith, and R. S. Reiserer (Eds.), *Rattlesnakes of Arizona, vol. 1*. ECO Publishing, Rodeo, New Mexico.

Diller, L. V., and R. L. Wallace (1996). Comparative ecology of two snake species (*Crotalus viridis* and *Pituophis melanoleucas*) in southwestern Idaho. Herpetologica 52: 343–360.

Douglas, M. E., M. R. Douglas, G. W. Schuett, L. W. Porras, and A. T. Holycross (2002). Phylogeography of the Western Rattlesnake (*Crotalus viridis complex*), with emphasis on the Colorado Plateau. Pp. 11–50 *In* G. W. Schuett, M. Höggren, M. E. Douglas, and H. W. Greene (Eds.), *Biology of the Vipers*. Eagle Mountain Publishing, LC, Eagle Mountain, Utah.

Douglas, M. E., M. R. Douglas, G. W. Schuett, and L. W. Porras (2006). Evolution of rattle-snakes (Viperidae; *Crotalus*) in the warm deserts of western North America shaped by Neogene vicariance and Quaternary climate change. Molecular Ecology 15: 3,353–3,374.

Douglas, M. E., M. R. Douglas, G. W. Schuett, L. W. Porras, and B. L. Thomason (2007). Genea-logical concordance between mitochondrial and nuclear DNAs supports species recog-nition of the Panamint Rattlesnake (*Crotalus mitchellii stephensi*). Copeia 2007: 920–932.

Douglas, M. R., M. A. Davis, M. Amarello, J. J. Smith, G. W. Schuett, H.-W. Herrmann, and M. E. Douglas (2016). Anthropogenic impacts drive conservation and ecosystem metrics of a niche conserved rattlesnake on the Colorado Plateau of Western North America. Royal Society Open Science 3: 160047.

Dreslik, M. J., W. K. Hayes, S. J. Beaupre, and S. P. Mackessy (2017). *The Biology of Rattle-snakes II*. ECO Publishing, Rodeo, New Mexico.

Durham, F. E. (1956). Amphibians and reptiles of the North Rim, Grand Canyon, Arizona. Herpetologica 12: 220–224.

Duvall, D., and G. W. Schuett (1997). Straight-line movement and competitive mate search-ing in Prairie Rattlesnakes, *Crotalus viridis viridis*. Animal Behaviour 54: 329–334.

Duvall, D., S. J. Arnold, and G. W. Schuett (1992). Pitviper mating systems: Ecological poten-tial, sexual selection, and microevolution. Pp. 321–336 *In* J. A. Campbell, and E. D. Brodie Jr. (Eds.), *Biology of the Pitvipers*. Selva, Tyler, Texas.

Duvall, D., M. B. King, and K. J. Gutzwiller (1985). Behavioral ecology and ethology of the Prairie Rattlesnake. National Geographic Research 1: 80–111.

Duvall, D., M. J. Goode, W. K. Hayes, J. K. Leonhardt, and D. G. Brown (1990). Prairie Rattle-snake vernal migration: Field experimental analyses and survival value. National Geo-graphic Research 6: 457–469.

Ernst, C. H., and E. M Ernst (2012). *Venomous Reptiles of the United States, Canada, and Northern Mexico*, 2 vols. The Johns Hopkins University Press, Baltimore, Maryland.

Feldner, M. J., G. W. Schuett, and J. M. Slone (2016a). Species Accounts. *Crotalus abyssus* (Grand Canyon Rattlesnake). Pp. 45–108 *In* In G. W. Schuett, M. J. Feldner, C. F. Smith, and R. S. Reiserer (Eds.), *Rattlesnakes of Arizona, vol. 1*. ECO Publishing, Rodeo, New Mexico.

Feldner, M. J., G. W. Schuett, and J. M. Slone (2016b). Species Accounts. *Crotalus concolor* (Midget Faded Rattlesnake). Pp. 179–238 *In* G. W. Schuett, M. J. Feldner, C. F. Smith, and R. S. Reiserer (Eds.), *Rattlesnakes of Arizona, vol. 1*. ECO Publishing, Rodeo, New Mexico.

Feldner, M. J., G. W. Schuett, and J. M. Slone (2016c). Species Accounts. *Crotalus lutosus* (Great Basin Rattlesnake). Pp. 239–288 *In* G. W. Schuett, M. J. Feldner, C. F. Smith, and R. S. Reiserer (Eds.), *Rattlesnakes of Arizona, vol. 1*. ECO Publishing, Rodeo, New Mexico.

Gardiner, L. E., C. M. Somers, D. L. Parker, and R. G. Poulin (2015). Microhabitat selection by Prairie Rattlesnakes (*Crotalus viridis*) at the northern extreme of their geographic range. Journal of Herpetology 49: 131–137.

Glaudas, X., and J. A. Rodríguez-Robles (2011a). Vagabond males and sedentary females: Spatial ecology and mating system of the Speckled Rattlesnake (*Crotalus mitchellii*). Biological Journal of the Linnean Society 103: 681–695.

Glaudas, X., and J. A. Rodríguez-Robles. (2011b). A two-level problem: Habitat selection in relation to prey abundance in an ambush predator, the Speckled Rattlesnake (*Crotalus mitchellii*). Behaviour 148: 1,491–1,524.

Glaudas, X., S. R. Goldberg, and B. T. Hamilton (2009). Timing of reproduction of a cold desert viperid snake from North America, the Great Basin Rattlesnake (*Crotalus lutosus*). Journal of Arid Environments 73: 719–725.

Gloyd, H. K. (1940). *The Rattlesnakes. Genera* Sistrurus and Crotalus. *A Study in Zoögraphy and Evolution*. Special Publication No. 4, Chicago Academy of Sciences, Chicago, Illinois.

Hardy, D. L., and H. W. Greene (1995). Natural History Notes. *Crotalus molossus molossus* (Blacktail Rattlesnake). Maximum length. Herpetological Review 26: 101.

Hardy, D. L., and K. R. Zamudio (2006). Compartment syndrome, fasciotomy, and neuropathy after a rattlesnake envenomation: Aspects of monitoring and diagnosis. Wilderness Environmental Medicine 17: 26–40.

Herrmann, H.-W. (2016). A molecular perspective on conservation: Rattlesnakes as models. Pp. 461–485 *In* G. W. Schuett, M. J. Feldner, C. F. Smith, and R. S. Reiserer (Eds.), *Rattlesnakes of Arizona, vol. 2*. ECO Publishing, Rodeo, New Mexico.

Jones, L. L. C. (2016). The spelling of Mojave vs. Mohave as it applies to standard English names for reptiles and amphibians. Sonoran Herpetologist 29(4): 65–71.

Klauber, L. M. (1930). New and renamed subspecies of *Crotalus confluentus* Say, with remarks on related species. Transactions of the San Diego Society of Natural History 6: 95–144.

Klauber, L. M. (1932). A Herpetological Review of the Hopi Snake Dance. Zoological Society of San Diego Bulletin 9: 1–92.

Klauber, L. M. (1935). A new subspecies of *Crotalus confluentus*, the Prairie Rattlesnake. Transactions of the San Diego Society of Natural History 8: 75–90.

Klauber, L. M. (1936). A key to the rattlesnakes with summary of characters. Transactions of the San Diego Society of Natural History 8: 185–276.

Klauber, L. M. (1972). *Rattlesnakes. Their Habits, Life History and Influence on Mankind*, 2 vols., 2nd edn. University of California Press, Los Angeles and Berkeley, California.

Mackessy, S. P. (2008). Venom composition in rattlesnakes: Trends and biological significance. Pp. 495–510 *In* W. K. Hayes, K. R. Beaman, M. D. Cardwell, and S. P. Bush (Eds.), *The Biology of Rattlesnakes*. Loma Linda University Press, Loma Linda, California.

Mackessy, S. P. (2010). Evolutionary trends in venom composition in the Western Rattlesnakes (*Crotalus viridis* sensu lato): Toxicity vs. tenderizers. Toxicon 55: 1463–1474.

Mackessy, S. P., and T. A. Castoe (2016). Deciphering the evolution of venom and the venom apparatus in rattlesnakes. Pp. 57–90 *In* G. W. Schuett, M. J. Feldner, C. F. Smith, and R. S. Reiserer (Eds.), *Rattlesnakes of Arizona, vol. 2*. ECO Publishing, Rodeo, New Mexico.

Mackessy, S. P., K. Williams, and K. G. Ashton (2003). Ontogenetic variation in venom composition and diet of *Crotalus oreganus concolor*: A case of venom paedomorphosis? Copeia 2003: 769–782.

Malhotra, A., S. Creer, C. E. Pook, and R. S. Thorpe. 2010. Inclusion of nuclear intron sequence data helps to identify the Asian sister group of New World pitvipers. Molecular Phylogenetics and Evolution 54: 172–178.

McDiarmid, R. W., J. A. Campbell, and T. A. Toure (1999). Snake Species of the World: A Taxonomic and Geographic History, Volume 1. Herpetologists' League, Washington, District of Columbia.

Mead, J. I., and T. R. Van Devender (1981). Late Holocene diet of *Bassariscus astutus* in the Grand Canyon, Arizona. J. Mammal. 62: 439–442.

Meik, J. M. (2016). Species Accounts. *Crotalus pyrrhus* (Southwestern Speckled Rattlesnake). Pp. 531–562 *In* G. W. Schuett, M. J. Feldner, C. F. Smith, and R. S. Reiserer (Eds.), *Rattlesnakes of Arizona, vol. 1*. ECO Publishing, Rodeo, New Mexico.

Meik, J. M., and G. W. Schuett (2016). Structure, ontogeny, and evolutionary development of the rattlesnake rattle. Pp. 277–300 *In* G. W. Schuett, M. J. Feldner, C. F. Smith, and R. S. Reiserer (Eds.), *Rattlesnakes of Arizona, vol. 2*. ECO Publishing, Rodeo, New Mexico.

Miller, D. M., R. A. Young, T. W. Gatlin, and J. A. Richardson (1982). *Amphibians and Reptiles of the Grand Canyon*. Grand Canyon Natural History Association, Monograph No. 4.

Mrinalini, J., R. Hicks, and W. Wüster. (2015). Natural History Notes. *Crotalus scutulatus* (Mohave Rattlesnake). Maximum size. Herpetological Review 46: 271.

Nowak, E. M., and H. W. Greene (2016). Rattlesnake conservation in the 21st century. Pp. 413–458 *In* G. W. Schuett, M. J. Feldner, C. F. Smith, and R. S. Reiserer (Eds.), *Rattlesnakes of Arizona, vol. 2*. ECO Publishing, Rodeo, New Mexico.

Nowak, E. M., and G. W. Schuett (2016). Syntopy in rattlesnakes: A case study from Arizona. Pp. 367–409 *In* G. W. Schuett, M. J. Feldner, C. F. Smith, and R. S. Reiserer (Eds.), *Rattlesnakes of Arizona, vol. 2*. ECO Publishing, Rodeo, New Mexico.

Parker, J. M., and S. H. Anderson (2007). Ecology and behavior of the Midget Faded Rattlesnake (*Crotalus oreganus concolor*) in Wyoming. Journal of Herpetology 41: 41–51.

Parker, W. S., and W. S. Brown (1973). Species composition and population changes in two complexes of snake hibernacula in northern Utah. Herpetologica 29: 319–326.

Persons, T. B., M. J. Feldner, and R. A. Repp (2016). Species Accounts. *Crotalus molossus* (Black-tailed Rattlesnake). Pp. 461–505 *In* G. W. Schuett, M. J. Feldner, C. F. Smith, and R. S. Reiserer (Eds.), *Rattlesnakes of Arizona, vol. 1*. ECO Publishing, Rodeo, New Mexico.

Pook, C. E., W. Wüster, and R. S. Thorpe (2000). Historical biogeography of the Western Rattlesnake (Serpentes: Viperidae: *Crotalus viridis*), inferred from mitochondrial DNA sequence information. Molecular Phylogenetics & Evolution 15: 269–282.

Porras, L. W., L. D. Wilson, G. W. Schuett, and R. S. Reiserer (2013). A taxonomic reevaluation and conservation assessment of the common cantil, *Agkistrodon bilineatus* (Squamata: Viperidae): A race against time. Amphibian & Reptile Conservation 7: 48–73.

Quinn, H. R. (1987). Morphology, Isozymes, and Mitochondrial DNA as Systematic Indicators in *Crotalus*. Unpublished dissertation. University of Houston, University Park, Texas.

Reed, R. N., and M. E. Douglas (2002). Ecology of the Grand Canyon Rattlesnake (*Crotalus viridis abyssus*) in the Little Colorado River Canyon, Arizona. Southwestern Naturalist 47: 30–39.

Reiserer, R. S. (2016). Art and rattlesnakes. Pp. 21–37 *In* G. W. Schuett, M. J. Feldner, C. F. Smith, and R. S. Reiserer (Eds.), *Rattlesnakes of Arizona, vol. 1*. ECO Publishing, Rodeo, New Mexico.

Reiserer, R. S., and G. W. Schuett (2016). The origin and evolution of the rattlesnake rattle: Misdirection, clarification, theory, and progress. Pp. 245–274 *In* G. W. Schuett, M. J. Feldner, C. F. Smith, and R. S. Reiserer (Eds.), *Rattlesnakes of Arizona, vol. 2*. ECO Publishing, Rodeo, New Mexico.

Schield, D. R., D. C. Card, J. Reyes-Velasco, A. L. Andrew et al. (2016). A role for genomics in rattlesnake research – current knowledge and future potential. Pp. 33–56 *In* G. W. Schuett, M. J. Feldner, C. F. Smith, and R. S. Reiserer (Eds.), *Rattlesnakes of Arizona, vol. 2*. ECO Publishing, Rodeo, New Mexico.

Schuett, G. W., S. L. Carlisle, A. T. Holycross, J. K. O'Leile, D. L. Hardy, E. A. Van Kirk, and W. J. Murdoch (2002). Mating system of male Mojave Rattlesnakes (*Crotalus scutulatus*): Seasonal timing of mating, agonistic behavior, spermatogenesis, sexual segment of the kidney, and plasma sex steroids. Pp. 515–532 *In* G. W. Schuett, M. Höggren, M. E. Douglas, and H. W. Greene (Eds.), *Biology of the Vipers*. Eagle Mountain Publishing, LC, Eagle Mountain, Utah.

Schuett, G. W., R. A. Repp, C. L. Spencer, K. Beamann, and C. W. Painter (2016a). Species Accounts. *Crotalus atrox* (Western Diamond-backed Rattlesnake). Pp. 333–394 *In* G. W. Schuett, M. J. Feldner, C. F. Smith, and R. S. Reiserer (Eds.), *Rattlesnakes of Arizona, vol. 1*. ECO Publishing, Rodeo, New Mexico.

Schuett G. W., R. W. Clark, R. A. Repp, M. Amarello, C. F. Smith, and H. W. Greene (2016b). Social behavior of rattlesnakes: A shifting paradigm, Pp. 161–244 *In* G. W. Schuett, M. J. Feldner, C. F. Smith, and R. S. Reiserer (Eds.), *Rattlesnakes of Arizona, vol. 2*. ECO Publishing, Rodeo, New Mexico.

Shipley, B. K., D. Chiszar, K. T. Fitzgerald, and A. J. Saviola. (2013). Spatial ecology of Prairie Rattlesnakes (*Crotalus viridis*) associated with Black-tailed Prairie Dog (*Cynomys ludovicianus*) colonies in Colorado. Herpetological Conservation and Biology 8: 240–250.

SSAR. (2017). *Scientific and Standard English Names of Amphibians and Reptiles of North America North of Mexico, With Comments Regarding Confidence in Our Understanding. 8th Edition*. Committee on Standard English and Scientific Names. Brian I. Crother (Committee Chair). SSAR Herpetological Circular No. 43, Shoreview, Minnesota.

Spencer, C. L. (2003). Geographic Variation in the Morphology, Diet and Reproduction of a Widespread Pitviper, the Western Diamondback Rattlesnake (*Crotalus atrox*). Unpublished dissertation, The University of Texas, Arlington, Texas.

Taylor, E. and W. Booth (2016). Rattlesnakes as models of reproductive studies of vertebrates. Pp. 121–160 *In* G. W. Schuett, M. J. Feldner, C. F. Smith, and R. S. Reiserer (Eds.), *Rattlesnakes of Arizona, vol. 2*. ECO Publishing, Rodeo, New Mexico.

Wüster, W. (2016). Recent developments in rattlesnake phylogenetics, phylogeography and species delimitation models. Pp. 9–29 *In* G. W. Schuett, M. J. Feldner, C. F. Smith, and R. S. Reiserer (Eds.), *Rattlesnakes of Arizona, vol. 2*. ECO Publishing, Rodeo, New Mexico.

Young, R. A., and D. M. Miller (1980). Notes on the natural history of the Grand Canyon Rattlesnake, *Crotalus viridis abyssus* Klauber. Bulletin of the Chicago Herpetological Society 15: 1–5.

Zancolli, G., T. G. Baker, A. Barlow, R. K. Bradley et al. (2016). Is hybridization a source of adaptive venom variation in rattlesnakes? A test using a *Crotalus scutulatus viridis* hybrid zone in Southwestern New Mexico. Toxins 8(6): 188. doi:10.3390/toxins8060188.

Glossary

Antivenin (antivenom). An antidote containing antibodies against specific venoms of snakes. In the Grand Canyon region, antivenin is used for rattlesnake bites.

Biological species Concept (BSC). The BSC is the most widely accepted species concept. It defines species in terms of interbreeding. Species, therefore, can be defined as a population of interbreeding individuals that are cohesive and reproductively isolated from other such populations.

Convergent Evolution. In biology, convergence is the condition where distantly related organisms (e.g., American horned lizards *vs.* Australian thorny lizard) independently evolve similar traits as a result of adaptation to similar environments.

Evolution. Darwin (1859) defined evolution as modification with descent. Today, evolution is defined as change in the heritable (genetic) characteristics of individuals of a population over successive generations.

Hemotoxic Venom. Many species of rattlesnakes produce venoms that are predominately hemotoxic. This category of venoms can cause hemolysis, disrupt clotting, and adversely affect other types of cells and tissues. Bites from species with hemotoxic venoms often result in severe tissue damage and are sometimes implicated in organ failure. See **Venom; Neurotoxic Venom**.

Lineage. Lineages In evolutionary biology are organisms (populations) connected by a continuous line of descent from a most-recent common ancestor to all of its descendents.

Mitochondrial DNA Sequence. Sequence information (precise order of nucleotides of genes) derived from mtDNA (the DNA located in mitochondria, which are located in cytoplasm) and used in phylogenetic analysis of organisms. See **Nuclear DNA Sequence**.

Morphological Species Concept (MSC). The MSC defines a species by body shape and other structural features; it is applied both to asexual and sexual organisms, especially when information on interbreeding, gene flow, and other genetic information is unknown. The only concept used for diagnosing species that are extinct and fossilized. See **BSC.**

Neurotoxic Venom. Several species of rattlesnakes produce venoms that are predominately neurotoxic. This category of venoms can cause neurotoxicity, paralytic effects mediated at the neuromuscular junction and organ failure, and other insults that are life-threatening. In rattlesnakes, two well-known venom neurotoxins are mojave-toxin and concolor-toxin. See **Venom; Hemotoxic Venom**.

Nuclear DNA Sequence. Sequence information of DNA contained within the nucleus of a eukaryotic organism. See **Mitochondrial DNA Sequence**.

Parthenogenesis. A type of asexual reproduction in which an unfertilized ovum can develop directly into a new individual without a male (i.e., spermatozoa). Several forms of parthenogenesis ("virgin birth") are known in reptiles; one type occurs in rattlesnakes and other snakes (i.e., facultative parthenogenesis).

Petroglyph. In this book, an image (art, language) carved, incised, or scratched into stone made by ancient indigenous Americans. See **Pictograph**.

Phylogenetic Species Concept (PSC). The PSC defines a species as an irreducible population whose members (individuals) are descended from a most-recent common ancestor which possess a one or more defining characters called shared-derived traits (e.g., apomorphies). See **BSC** and **MSC**.

Phylogeny (phylogenetic). The concept of phylogeny in its simplest terms is the evolutionary (deep) history of any kind of organism.

Pictograph. In this book, a pictograph is a symbolic painting (art, language) found in caves made by ancient indigenous Americans. These images are made from natural pigments. If exposed they are vulnerable to the elements (e.g., sun, wind-blown sand, and precipitation). See **Petroglyph**.

Poison (poisonous). A noxious (capable of causing illness or death) substance produced by an organism that gains entry via ingestion. Other entry ways of poisons include the eyes, ears, and skin. See **Venom**.

Species. There are multiple views on the definition of a species. Three commonly used ones (not necessarily mutually exclusive) by professional biologists are the Biological species Concept (BSC), Morphological Species Concept (MSC), and Phylogenetic Species Concept (PSC).

Venom (venomous). A noxious substance (e.g., proteins) capable of causing illness or death when it gains entry into prey, an aggressor or enemy, by way of biting (e.g., fangs) or stinging. See **Antivenin** and **Poison**.

Authors

Dr. Gordon W. Schuett is an evolutionary biologist and behavioral ecologist. He has conducted extensive laboratory and field research on reptiles, primarily focused on venomous snakes, but also has published on lizards, turtles, and amphibians. His most significant contributions cover topics on mate competition and winner-loser effects, long-term sperm storage, mating systems, seasonal steroid hormone cycles of pitvipers, and facultative parthenogenesis in snakes. He is senior editor of the peer-reviewed book, *Biology of the Vipers* (Eagle Mountain Publishing, 2002) and senior editor of the peer-reviewed book (2 volumes), *Rattlesnakes of Arizona* (ECO Publishing, 2016). Gordon is an Adjunct Professor of Biology at Georgia State University and Director of the Scientific Advisory Board of the Chiricahua Desert Museum.

Dr. Charles F. Smith is an evolutionary biologist and herpetologist. His research interests center on the evolution of mating systems, especially in the links between spatial ecology, behavior, morphology and physiology, and the fitness benefits and costs arising from each of these attributes at the population level. Chuck's research combines field (e.g., radio-telemetry, GIS analysis) and laboratory (e.g., endocrinological, histological, molecular) approaches to address hypotheses about the spatial ecology and reproductive physiology of pitvipers. Chuck is a Professor of Biology at Wofford College, Director of The Copperhead Institute, a member of the Scientific Advisory Board of the Chiricahua Desert Museum, and co-editor of the peer-reviewed book (2 volumes), *Rattlesnakes of Arizona* (ECO Publishing, 2016).

Bob Ashley was born in Michigan and grew up in East Grand Rapids. He spent his youth catching turtles and snakes in the nearby swamps and fields and was an active member of the Michigan Society of Herpetologists. Bob started ECO Wear and Publishing in 1995 offering custom T-shirt designs, wildlife art, and custom books. To date, ECO has published over 40 books on reptile and amphibian natural history and husbandry. Bob is the Past President of the International Herpetological Symposium and the current Vice President. Bob opened the Chiricahua Desert Museum in 2009 (Rodeo, New Mexico). This facility is an educational exhibit of reptiles and amphibians from the Western Hemisphere associated with the deserts of the Southwestern United States and Mexico, with a focus on rattlesnakes of the Sky Islands.